www.EffortlessMath.com

... So Much More Online!

✓ FREE Math lessons

✓ More Math learning books!

✓ Mathematics Worksheets

✓ Online Math Tutors

Need a PDF version of this book?

Send email to: Info@EffortlessMath.com

Prepare for the ALEKS Math Test in 7 Days

A Quick Study Guide with Two Full-Length ALEKS Math Practice Tests

By

Reza Nazari & Ava Ross

All inquiries should be addressed to:

info@effortlessMath.com

www.EffortlessMath.com

ISBN–13: 978-1-64612-126-7

ISBN–10: 1-64612-126-0

Published by: Effortless Math Education

www.EffortlessMath.com

Description

Prepare for the ALEKS Math Test in 7 Days, which reflects the 2019 and 2020 test guidelines and topics, incorporates the best method and the right strategies to help you hone your math skills, overcome your exam anxiety, and boost your confidence -- and do your best to defeat ALEKS Math test quickly. This quick study guide contains only the most important and critical math concepts a student will need in order to succeed on the ALEKS Math test. Math concepts in this book break down the topics, so the material can be quickly grasped. Examples are worked step–by–step to help you learn exactly what to do.

This ALEKS Math new edition has been updated to duplicate questions appearing on the most recent ALEKS Math tests. It contains easy–to–read essential summaries that highlight the key areas of the ALEKS Math test. You only need to spend about 3 – 5 hours daily in your 7–day period in order to achieve your goal. After reviewing this book, you will have solid foundation and adequate practice that is necessary to fully prepare for the ALEKS Math.

Prepare for the ALEKS Math Test in 7 Days is for all ALEKS Math test takers. It is a breakthrough in Math learning — offering a winning formula and the most powerful methods for learning basic Math topics confidently. Each section offers step–by–step instruction and helpful hints, with a few topics being tackled each day.

Inside the pages of this comprehensive book, students can learn math topics in a structured manner with a complete study program to help them understand essential math skills. It also has many exciting features, including:

- Content 100% aligned with the 2019-2020 ALEKS test
- Written by ALEKS Math tutors and test experts
- Complete coverage of all ALEKS Math concepts and topics which you will be tested
- Step-by-step guide for all ALEKS Math topics
- Dynamic design and easy-to-follow activities
- Over 1,500 additional ALEKS math practice questions in both multiple-choice and grid-in formats with answers grouped by topic, so you can focus on your weak areas
- 2 full-length practice tests (featuring new question types) with detailed answers

Effortlessly and confidently follow the step–by–step instructions in this book to prepare for the ALEKS Math in a short period of time.

Prepare for the ALEKS Math Test in 7 Days is the only book you'll ever need to master Basic Math topics! It can be used as a self–study course – you do not need to work with a Math tutor. (It can also be used with a Math tutor).

Ideal for self–study as well as for classroom usage.

About the Author

Reza Nazari is the author of more than 100 Math learning books including:
– **Math and Critical Thinking Challenges:** For the Middle and High School Student
– **GRE Math in 30 Days**
– **ASVAB Math Workbook 2018 - 2019**
– **Effortless Math Education Workbooks**
– **and many more Mathematics books …**

Reza is also an experienced Math instructor and a test–prep expert who has been tutoring students since 2008. Reza is the founder of Effortless Math Education, a tutoring company that has helped many students raise their standardized test scores—and attend the colleges of their dreams. Reza provides an individualized custom learning plan and the personalized attention that makes a difference in how students view math.

You can contact Reza via email at:
reza@EffortlessMath.com

Find Reza's professional profile at:
goo.gl/zoC9rJ

Contents

Day 1:
Integers, Ratios, and Proportions

Math Topics that you'll learn today:

- ✓ Adding and Subtracting Integers
- ✓ Multiplying and Dividing Integers
- ✓ Order of Operations
- ✓ Integers and Absolute Value
- ✓ Simplifying Ratios
- ✓ Proportional Ratios
- ✓ Similarity and Ratios

"Without mathematics, there's nothing you can do. Everything around you is mathematics. Everything around you is numbers." – Shakuntala Devi

Adding and Subtracting Integers

Step-by-step guide:

- ✓ Integers includes: zero, counting numbers, and the negative of the counting numbers. $\{..., -3, -2, -1, 0, 1, 2, 3, ...\}$
- ✓ Add a positive integer by moving to the right on the number line.
- ✓ Add a negative integer by moving to the left on the number line.
- ✓ Subtract an integer by adding its opposite.

Examples:

1) Solve. $(-8) - (-5) =$

Keep the first number and convert the sign of the second number to its opposite. (change subtraction into addition. Then: $(-8) + 5 = -3$

2) Solve. $10 + (4 - 8) =$

First subtract the numbers in brackets, $4 - 8 = -4$

Then: $10 + (-4) = \ \rightarrow$ change addition into subtraction: $10 - 4 = 6$

Multiplying and Dividing Integers

Step-by-step guide:

Use these rules for multiplying and dividing integers:

- ✓ (negative) × (negative) = positive
- ✓ (negative) ÷ (negative) = positive
- ✓ (negative) × (positive) = negative
- ✓ (negative) ÷ (positive) = negative
- ✓ (positive) × (positive) = positive

Examples:

1) Solve. $(2 - 5) \times (3) =$

First subtract the numbers in brackets, $2 - 5 = -3 \rightarrow (-3) \times (3) =$

Now use this formula: (negative) × (positive) = negative
$(-3) \times (3) = -9$

2) Solve. $(-12) + (48 \div 6) =$

First divided 48 by 6 , the numbers in brackets, $48 \div 6 = 8$

$= (-12) + (8) = -12 + 8 = -4$

Order of Operations

Step-by-step guide:

When there is more than one math operation, use PEMDAS:

✓ Parentheses

✓ Exponents

✓ Multiplication and Division (from left to right)

✓ Addition and Subtraction (from left to right)

Examples:

1) Solve. $(5 + 7) \div (3^2 \div 3) =$

First simplify inside parentheses: $(12) \div (9 \div 3) = (12) \div (3) =$
Then: $(12) \div (3) = 4$

2) Solve. $(11 \times 5) - (12 - 7) =$

First simplify inside parentheses: $(11 \times 5) - (12 - 7) = (55) - (5) =$

Then: $(55) - (5) = 50$

Integers and Absolute Value

Step-by-step guide:

- ✓ To find an absolute value of a number, just find its distance from 0 on number line! For example, the distance of 12 and -12 from zero on number line is 12!

Examples:

1) Solve. $\frac{|-18|}{9} \times |5 - 8| =$

First find $|-18|$, →the absolute value of -18 is 18, then: $|-18| = 18$

$\frac{18}{9} \times |5 - 8| =$

Next, solve $|5 - 8|$, → $|5 - 8| = |-3|$, the absolute value of -3 is 3. $|-3| = 3$

Then: $\frac{18}{9} \times 3 = 2 \times 3 = 6$

2) Solve. $|10 - 5| \times \frac{|-2 \times 6|}{3} =$

First solve $|10 - 5|$, → $|10 - 5| = |5|$, the absolute value of 5 is 5, $|5| = 5$

$5 \times \frac{|-2 \times 6|}{3} =$

Now solve $|-2 \times 6|$, → $|-2 \times 6| = |-12|$, the absolute value of -12 is 12, $|-12| = 12$

Then: $5 \times \frac{12}{3} = 5 \times 4 = 20$

Simplifying Ratios

Step-by-step guide:

- ✓ Ratios are used to make comparisons between two numbers.
- ✓ Ratios can be written as a fraction, using the word "to", or with a colon.
- ✓ You can calculate equivalent ratios by multiplying or dividing both sides of the ratio by the same number.

Examples:

1) Simplify. $8 : 4 =$

Both numbers 8 and 4 are divisible by 4, $\Rightarrow 8 \div 4 = 2, 4 \div 4 = 1,$

Then: $8 : 4 = 2 : 1$

2) Simplify. $\frac{12}{36} =$

Both numbers 12 and 36 are divisible by 12, $\Rightarrow$ $12 \div 12 = 1$, $36 \div 12 = 3$,

Then: $\dfrac{12}{36} = \dfrac{1}{3}$

Proportional Ratios

Step-by-step guide:

- ✓ A proportion means that two ratios are equal. It can be written in two ways:
  $\dfrac{a}{b} = \dfrac{c}{d}$, $a : b = c : d$
- ✓ The proportion $\dfrac{a}{b} = \dfrac{c}{d}$ can be written as: $a \times d = c \times b$

Examples:

1) Solve this proportion for x. $\dfrac{4}{8} = \dfrac{5}{x}$

   Use cross multiplication: $\dfrac{4}{8} = \dfrac{5}{x} \Rightarrow 4 \times x = 5 \times 8 \Rightarrow 4x = 40$

   Divide to find x: $\quad x = \dfrac{40}{4} \Rightarrow x = 10$

2) If a box contains red and blue balls in ratio of $2:3$ red to blue, how many red balls are there if 90 blue balls are in the box?

   Write a proportion and solve. $\dfrac{2}{3} = \dfrac{x}{90}$
   Use cross multiplication: $2 \times 90 = 3 \times x \Rightarrow 180 = 3x$
   Divide to find x: $\qquad x = \dfrac{180}{3} \Rightarrow x = 60$

Similarity and Ratios

Step-by-step guide:

- ✓ Two or more figures are similar if the corresponding angles are equal, and the corresponding sides are in proportion.

Examples:

1) A girl $160\ cm$ tall, stands $360\ cm$ from a lamp post at night. Her shadow from the light is $90\ cm$ long. How high is the lamp post?

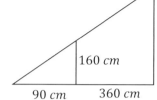

Write the proportion and solve for missing side.

$$\frac{\text{Smaller triangle height}}{\text{Smaller triangle base}} = \frac{\text{Bigger triangle height}}{\text{Bigger triangle base}}$$

$$\Rightarrow \frac{90cm}{160cm} = \frac{90+360cm}{x} \Rightarrow 90x = 160 \times 450 \Rightarrow x = 800\ cm$$

2) A tree $32\ feet$ tall casts a shadow $12\ feet$ long. Jack is $6\ feet$ tall. How long is Jack's shadow?

Write a proportion and solve for the missing number.

$$\frac{32}{12} = \frac{6}{x} \Rightarrow 32x = 6 \times 12 = 72 \Rightarrow 32x = 72 \rightarrow x = \frac{72}{32} = 2.25\ feet$$

Day 1 Practices

 Find each sum or difference.

1) $15 + (-8) =$

2) $(-11) + (-21) =$

3) $7 + (-27) =$

4) $45 + (-14) =$

5) $(-8) + (-12) + 6 =$

6) $37 + (-16) + 12 =$

 Find each product or quotient.

7) $(-7) \times (-8) =$

8) $4 \times (-5) =$

9) $5 \times (-11) =$

10) $(-5) \times (-20) =$

11) $-(2) \times (-8) \times 3 =$

12) $(12 - 4) \times (-10) =$

 Evaluate each expression.

13) $5 + (6 \times 3) =$

14) $13 - (2 \times 5) =$

15) $(14 \times 2) + 18 =$

16) $(12 - 5) - (4 \times 3) =$

17) $25 + (14 \div 2) =$

18) $(18 \times 5) \div 2 =$

 Evaluate the value.

19) $8 - |4 - 18| - |-2| =$

20) $|-2| - \frac{|-20|}{4} =$

21) $\frac{|-66|}{11} \times |-6| =$

22) $\frac{|-5 \times -3|}{5} \times \frac{|-20|}{4} =$

23) $|2 \times -4| + \frac{|-40|}{5} =$

24) $\frac{|-28|}{4} \times \frac{|-55|}{11} =$

Reduce each ratio.

25) $24 : 16 =$ ___ : ___

26) $4 : 40 =$ ___ : ___

27) $6 : 72 =$ ___ : ___

28) $18 : 36 =$ ___ : ___

29) $6 : 100 =$ ___ : ___

30) $4 : 24 =$ ___ : ___

 Solve each proportion.

31) $\frac{4}{10} = \frac{14}{x}, x =$ ____

32) $\frac{2}{12} = \frac{7}{x}, x =$ ____

33) $\frac{3}{5} = \frac{27}{x}, x =$ ____

34) $\frac{1}{5} = \frac{x}{80}, x =$ ____

35) $\frac{3}{7} = \frac{x}{63}, x =$ ____

36) $\frac{2}{8} = \frac{13}{x}, x =$ ____

 Solve each problem.

37) Two rectangles are similar. The first is $6\ feet$ wide and $20\ feet$ long. The second is $15\ feet$ wide. What is the length of the second rectangle? _____

38) Two rectangles are similar. One is $2.5\ meters$ by $9\ meters$. The longer side of the second rectangle is $22.5\ meters$. What is the other side of the second rectangle?

_____

Answers

1) 7
2) −32
3) −20
4) 31
5) −14
6) 33
7) 56
8) −20
9) −55
10) 100
11) 48
12) −80
13) 23

14) 3
15) 46
16) −5
17) 32
18) 45
19) −8
20) −3
21) 36
22) 15
23) 16
24) 35
25) 3: 2
26) 1: 10

27) 1: 12
28) 1: 2
29) 3: 50
30) 1: 6
31) 35
32) 42
33) 45
34) 16
35) 27
36) 52
37) 50 feet
38) 6.25 meters

Day 2:
Percentage, Exponents, Variables and Roots

Math Topics that you'll learn today:

- ✓ Percentage Calculations
- ✓ Percent Problems
- ✓ Percent of Increase and Decrease
- ✓ Simple Interest
- ✓ Multiplication Property of Exponents
- ✓ Division Property of Exponents
- ✓ Powers of Products and Quotients
- ✓ Zero and Negative Exponents
- ✓ Negative Exponents and Negative Bases
- ✓ Scientific Notation
- ✓ Square Roots

Mathematics is no more computation than typing is literature. ‑ John Allen Paulos

Percentage Calculations

Step-by-step guide:

- ✓ Percent is a ratio of a number and 100. It always has the same denominator, 100. Percent symbol is %.
- ✓ Percent is another way to write decimals or fractions. For example:

$$40\% = 0.40 = \frac{40}{100} = \frac{2}{5}$$

- ✓ Use the following formula to find part, whole, or percent:

$$\text{part} = \frac{\text{percent}}{100} \times \text{whole}$$

Examples:

1) What is 10% of 45? Use the following formula: $\text{part} = \frac{\text{percent}}{100} \times \text{whole}$

$\text{part} = \frac{10}{100} \times 45 \;\rightarrow\; \text{part} = \frac{1}{10} \times 45 \;\rightarrow\; \text{part} = \frac{45}{10} \;\rightarrow\; \text{part} = 4.5$

2) What is 15% of 24? Use the percent formula: $\text{part} = \frac{\text{percent}}{100} \times \text{whole}$

$\text{part} = \frac{15}{100} \times 24 \;\rightarrow\; \text{part} = \frac{360}{100} \;\rightarrow\; \text{part} = 3.6$

Percent Problems

Step-by-step guide:

- ✓ In each percent problem, we are looking for the base, or part or the percent.
- ✓ Use the following equations to find each missing section.
  - ○ Base = Part ÷ Percent
  - ○ Part = Percent × Base
  - ○ Percent = Part ÷ Base

Examples:

1) 1.2 is what percent of 24?

In this problem, we are looking for the percent. Use the following equation:
$$Percent = Part \div Base \rightarrow Percent = 1.2 \div 24 = 0.05 = 5\%$$

2) 20 is 5% of what number?

Use the following formula: $Base = Part \div Percent \rightarrow Base = 20 \div 0.05 = 400$
20 is 5% of 400.

Percent of Increase and Decrease

Step-by-step guide:

To find the percentage of increase or decrease:
- ✓ New Number – Original Number
- ✓ The result ÷ Original Number × 100
- ✓ If your answer is a negative number, then this is a percentage decrease. If it is positive, then this is a percent of increase.

Examples:

1) Increased by 50%, the numbers 84 becomes:

First find 50% of 84 → $\frac{50}{100} \times 84 = \frac{50 \times 84}{100} = 42$

Then: $84 + 42 = 126$

2) The price of a shirt increases from $10 to $14. What is the percent increase?
First: $14 - 10 = 4$

4 is the result. Then: $4 \div 10 = \frac{4}{10} = 0.4 = 40\%$

Simple Interest

Step-by-step guide:

✓ Simple Interest: The charge for borrowing money or the return for lending it. To solve a simple interest problem, use this formula:

Interest = principal x rate x time $\Rightarrow$ $I = p \times r \times t$

Examples:

1) Find simple interest for $450 investment at 7% for 8 years.
Use Interest formula: $I = prt$, $P = \$450$, $r = 7\% = \frac{7}{100} = 0.07$ and $t = 8$
Then: $I = 450 \times 0.07 \times 8 = \$252$

2) Find simple interest for $5,200 at 4% for 3 years.

Use Interest formula: $I = prt$, $P = \$5,200$, $r = 4\% = \frac{4}{100} = 0.04$ and $t = 3$

Then: $I = 5,200 \times 0.04 \times 3 = \$624$

Multiplication Property of Exponents

Step-by-step guide:

- ✓ Exponents are shorthand for repeated multiplication of the same number by itself. For example, instead of 2×2, we can write 2^2. For $3 \times 3 \times 3 \times 3$, we can write 3^4
- ✓ In algebra, a variable is a letter used to stand for a number. The most common letters are: $x, y, z, a, b, c, m, and \; n$.
- ✓ Exponent's rules: $x^a \times x^b = x^{a+b}$, $\frac{x^a}{x^b} = x^{a-b}$

$$(x^a)^b = x^{a \times b}, \qquad (xy)^a = x^a \times y^a , (\frac{a}{b})^c = \frac{a^c}{b^c}$$

Examples:

1) Multiply. $-2x^5 \times 7x^3 =$
   Use Exponent's rules: $x^a \times x^b = x^{a+b} \rightarrow x^5 \times x^3 = x^{5+3} = x^8$
   Then: $-2x^5 \times 7x^3 = -14x^8$

2) Multiply. $(x^2 y^4)^3 =$
   Use Exponent's rules: $(x^a)^b = x^{a \times b}$. Then: $(x^2 \; y^4)^3 = x^{2 \times 3} y^{4 \times 3} = x^6 y^{12}$

Division Property of Exponents

Step-by-step guide:

- ✓ For division of exponents use these formulas: $\frac{x^a}{x^b} = x^{a-b}$, $x \neq 0$

$$\frac{x^a}{x^b} = \frac{1}{x^{b-a}} , x \neq 0, \qquad \frac{1}{x^b} = x^{-b}$$

Examples:

1) Simplify. $\dfrac{4x^3y}{36x^2y^3} =$

First cancel the common factor: $4 \rightarrow \dfrac{4x^3y}{36x^2y^3} = \dfrac{x^3y}{9x^2y^3}$

Use Exponent's rules: $\dfrac{x^a}{x^b} = x^{a-b} \rightarrow \dfrac{x^3}{x^2} = x^{3-2}$

Then: $\dfrac{4x^3y}{36x^2y^3} = \dfrac{xy}{9y^3} \rightarrow$ now cancel the common factor: $y \rightarrow \dfrac{xy}{9y^3} = \dfrac{x}{9y^2}$

2) Divide. $\dfrac{2x^{-5}}{9x^{-2}} =$

Use Exponent's rules: $\dfrac{x^a}{x^b} = \dfrac{1}{x^{b-a}} \rightarrow \dfrac{x^{-5}}{x^{-2}} = \dfrac{1}{x^{-2-(-5)}} = \dfrac{1}{x^{-2+5}} = \dfrac{1}{x^3}$

Then: $\dfrac{2x^{-5}}{9x^{-2}} = \dfrac{2}{9x^3}$

Powers of Products and Quotients

Step-by-step guide:

✓ For any nonzero numbers a and b and any integer x, $(ab)^x = a^x \times b^x$.

Examples:

1) Simplify. $(3x^5y^4)^2 =$

Use Exponent's rules: $(x^a)^b = x^{a \times b}$

$(3x^5y^4)^2 = (3)^2(x^5)^2(y^4)^2 = 9x^{5\times2}y^{4\times2} = 9x^{10}y^8$

2) Simplify. $\left(\dfrac{2x}{3x^2}\right)^2 =$ First cancel the common factor: $x \rightarrow \left(\dfrac{2x}{3x^2}\right)^2 = \left(\dfrac{2}{3x}\right)^2$

Use Exponent's rules: $\left(\dfrac{a}{b}\right)^c = \dfrac{a^c}{b^c}$,   Then: $\left(\dfrac{2}{3x}\right)^2 = \dfrac{2^2}{(3x)^2} = \dfrac{4}{9x^2}$

Zero and Negative Exponents

Step-by-step guide:

✓ A negative exponent simply means that the base is on the wrong side of the fraction line, so you need to flip the base to the other side. For instance, "x^{-2}" (pronounced as "ecks to the minus two") just means "x^2" but underneath, as in $\frac{1}{x^2}$.

Examples:

1) Evaluate. $\left(\frac{4}{9}\right)^{-2} =$

Use Exponent's rules: $\frac{1}{x^b} = x^{-b} \rightarrow \left(\frac{4}{9}\right)^{-2} = \frac{1}{\left(\frac{4}{9}\right)^2} = \frac{1}{\frac{4^2}{9^2}}$

Now use fraction rule: $\frac{1}{\frac{b}{c}} = \frac{c}{b} \rightarrow \frac{1}{\frac{4^2}{9^2}} = \frac{9^2}{4^2} = \frac{81}{16}$

2) Evaluate. $\left(\frac{5}{6}\right)^{-3} =$

Use Exponent's rules: $\frac{1}{x^b} = x^{-b} \rightarrow \left(\frac{5}{6}\right)^{-3} = \frac{1}{\left(\frac{5}{6}\right)^3} = \frac{1}{\frac{5^3}{6^3}}$

Now use fraction rule: $\frac{1}{\frac{b}{c}} = \frac{c}{b} \rightarrow \frac{1}{\frac{5^3}{6^3}} = \frac{6^3}{5^3} = \frac{216}{125}$

Negative Exponents and Negative Bases

Step-by-step guide:

✓ Make the power positive. A negative exponent is the reciprocal of that number with a positive exponent.

✓ The parenthesis is important!

✓ 5^{-2} is not the same as $(-5)^{-2}$

$$(-5)^{-2} = -\frac{1}{5^2} \text{ and } (-5)^{-2} = +\frac{1}{5^2}$$

Examples:

1) Simplify. $\left(\frac{3a}{2c}\right)^{-2} =$

Use Exponent's rules: $\frac{1}{x^b} = x^{-b} \rightarrow (\frac{3a}{2c})^{-2} = \frac{1}{(\frac{3a}{2c})^2} = \frac{1}{\frac{3^2 a^2}{2^2 c^2}}$

Now use fraction rule: $\frac{1}{\frac{b}{c}} = \frac{c}{b} \rightarrow \frac{1}{\frac{3^2 a^2}{2^2 c^2}} = \frac{2^2 c^2}{3^2 a^2}$

Then: $\frac{2^2 c^2}{3^2 a^2} = \frac{4c^2}{9a^2}$

2) Simplify. $(-\frac{5x}{3yz})^{-3} =$

Use Exponent's rules: $\frac{1}{x^b} = x^{-b} \rightarrow (-\frac{5x}{3yz})^{-3} = \frac{1}{(-\frac{5x}{3yz})^3} = \frac{1}{-\frac{5^3 x^3}{3^3 y^3 z^3}}$

Now use fraction rule: $\frac{1}{\frac{b}{c}} = \frac{c}{b} \rightarrow \frac{1}{-\frac{5^3 x^3}{3^3 y^3 z^3}} = -\frac{3^3 y^3 z^3}{5^3 x^3} = -\frac{27 y^3 z^3}{125 x^3}$

Scientific Notation

Step-by-step guide:

- ✓ It is used to write very big or very small numbers in decimal form.
- ✓ In scientific notation all numbers are written in the form of:

$$m \times 10^n$$

Decimal notation	Scientific notation
5	5×10^0
$-25,000$	-2.5×10^4
0.5	5×10^{-1}
2,122.456	2.122456×10^3

Examples:

1) Write 0.00012 in scientific notation.

First, move the decimal point to the right so that you have a number that is between 1 and 10. Then: $N = 1.2$

Second, determine how many places the decimal moved in step 1 by the power of 10.

Then: $10^{-4} \rightarrow$ When the decimal moved to the right, the exponent is negative.

Then: $0.00012 = 1.2 \times 10^{-4}$

2) Write 8.3×10^{-5} in standard notation.

$10^{-5} \rightarrow$ When the decimal moved to the right, the exponent is negative.

Then: $8.3 \times 10^{-5} = 0.000083$

Square Roots

Step-by-step guide:

- ✓ A square root of x is a number r whose square is: $r^2 = x$

    r is a square root of x.

Examples:

1) Find the square root of $\sqrt{225}$.

    First factor the number: $225 = 15^2$, Then: $\sqrt{225} = \sqrt{15^2}$

    Now use radical rule: $\sqrt[n]{a^n} = a$

    Then: $\sqrt{15^2} = 15$

2) Evaluate. $\sqrt{4} \times \sqrt{16} =$

    First factor the numbers: $4 = 2^2$ and $16 = 4^2$

    Then: $\sqrt{4} \times \sqrt{16} = \sqrt{2^2} \times \sqrt{4^2}$

    Now use radical rule: $\sqrt[n]{a^n} = a$, Then: $\sqrt{2^2} \times \sqrt{4^2} = 2 \times 4 = 8$

Day 2 Practices

 Calculate the given percent of each value.

1) 5% of 60 = ____

2) 10% of 30 = ____

3) 20% of 25 = ____

4) 50% of 80 = ____

5) 40% of 200 = ____

6) 20% of 45 = ____

 Solve each problem.

7) 20 is what percent of 50? ____%

8) 18 is what percent of 90? ____%

9) 12 is what percent of 15? ____%

10) 16 is what percent of 200? ____%

11) 24 is what percent of 800? ____%

12) 48 is what percent of 400? ____%

 Solve each percent of change word problem.

13) Bob got a raise, and his hourly wage increased from \$12 to \$15. What is the percent increase? _____ %

14) The price of a pair of shoes increases from \$20 to \$32. What is the percent increase? ____ %

 Determine the simple interest for these loans.

15) \$1,300 at 5% for 6 years.   \$ _____

16) \$5,400 at 3.5% for 6 months.   \$ _____

 Simplify and write the answer in exponential form.

17) $2yx^3 \times 4x^2y^3 =$

18) $4x^2 \times 9x^3y^4 =$

19) $7x^4y^5 \times 3x^2y^3 =$

20) $9x^2y^5 \times 7xy^3 =$

21) $4xy^4 \times 7x^3y^3 =$

22) $8x^2y^3 \times 3x^5y^3 =$

 Simplify. (Division Property of Exponents)

23) $\frac{3^7 \times 3^4}{3^8 \times 3^2} =$

24) $\frac{5x}{10x^3} =$

25) $\frac{6x^3}{4x^5} =$

26) $\frac{24x^3}{28x^6} =$

27) $\frac{24x^3}{18y^8} =$

28) $\frac{50xy^4}{10y^2} =$

✍ Simplify. (Powers of Products and Quotients)

29) $(9x^7y^5)^2 =$

30) $(4x^4y^6)^5 =$

31) $(3x \times 4y^3)^2 =$

32) $(\frac{5x}{x^2})^2 =$

33) $\left(\frac{x^4y^4}{x^2y^2}\right)^3 =$

34) $\left(\frac{25x}{5x^6}\right)^2 =$

✍ Evaluate the following expressions. (Zero and Negative Exponents)

35) $2^{-3} =$

36) $3^{-3} =$

37) $7^{-3} =$

38) $6^{-3} =$

39) $8^{-3} =$

40) $9^{-2} =$

✍ Simplify. (Negative Exponents and Negative Bases)

41) $-5x^{-2}y^{-3} =$

42) $20x^{-4}y^{-1} =$

43) $14a^{-6}b^{-7} =$

44) $-12x^2y^{-3} =$

45) $-\frac{25}{x^{-6}} =$

46) $\frac{7b}{-9c^{-4}} =$

✍ Write each number in scientific notation.

47) $0.000325 =$

48) $0.00023 =$

49) $56,000,000 =$

50) $21,000 =$

✍ Evaluate.

51) $\sqrt{9} \times \sqrt{4} =$ _____

52) $\sqrt{64} \times \sqrt{25} =$ _____

53) $\sqrt{8} \times \sqrt{2} =$ _____

54) $\sqrt{6} \times \sqrt{6} =$ _____

55) $\sqrt{5} \times \sqrt{5} =$ _____

56) $\sqrt{8} \times \sqrt{8} =$ _____

Answers

1) 3
2) 3
3) 5
4) 40
5) 80
6) 9
7) 40%
8) 20%
9) 80%
10) 8%
11) 3%
12) 12%
13) 25%
14) 60%
15) $390
16) $94.50
17) $8x^5y^4$
18) $36x^5y^4$
19) $21x^6y^8$
20) $63x^3y^8$
21) $28x^4y^7$

22) $24x^7y^6$
23) 3
24) $\frac{1}{2x^2}$
25) $\frac{3}{2x^2}$
26) $\frac{6}{7x^3}$
27) $\frac{4x^3}{3y^8}$
28) $5xy^2$
29) $81x^{14}y^{10}$
30) $1,024x^{20}y^{30}$
31) $144x^2y^6$
32) $\frac{25}{x^2}$
33) x^6y^6
34) $\frac{25}{x^{10}}$
35) $\frac{1}{8}$
36) $\frac{1}{27}$
37) $\frac{1}{343}$
38) $\frac{1}{216}$

39) $\frac{1}{512}$
40) $\frac{1}{81}$
41) $-\frac{5}{x^2y^3}$
42) $\frac{20}{x^4y}$
43) $\frac{14}{a^6b^7}$
44) $-\frac{12x^2}{y^3}$
45) $-25x^6$
46) $-\frac{7bc^4}{9}$
47) 3.25×10^{-4}
48) 2.3×10^{-4}
49) 5.6×10^7
50) 2.1×10^4
51) 6
52) 40
53) 4
54) 6
55) 5
56) 8

Day 3:
Expressions, Variables, Equations and Inequalities

Math Topics that you'll learn today:

- ✓ Simplifying Variable Expressions
- ✓ Simplifying Polynomial Expressions
- ✓ The Distributive Property
- ✓ Evaluating One Variable
- ✓ Evaluating Two Variables

- ✓ Combining like Terms
- ✓ One–Step Equations
- ✓ Multi–Step Equations
- ✓ Graphing Single–Variable Inequalities
- ✓ One–Step Inequalities
- ✓ Multi–Step Inequalities

Mathematics is, as it were, a sensuous logic, and relates to philosophy as do the arts, music, and plastic art to poetry. – K. Shegel

Simplifying Variable Expressions

Step-by-step guide:

- ✓ In algebra, a variable is a letter used to stand for a number. The most common letters are: $x, y, z, a, b, c, m, and\ n$.
- ✓ algebraic expression is an expression contains integers, variables, and the math operations such as addition, subtraction, multiplication, division, etc.
- ✓ In an expression, we can combine "like" terms. (values with same variable and same power)

Examples:

1) Simplify this expression. $(10x + 2x + 3) =$?
   Combine like terms. Then: $(10x + 2x + 3) = 12x + 3$ (remember you cannot combine variables and numbers.

2) Simplify this expression. $12 - 3x^2 + 9x + 5x^2 =$?
   Combine "like" terms: $-3x^2 + 5x^2 = 2x^2$

   Then: $12 - 3x^2 + 9x + 5x^2 = 12 + 2x^2 + 9x$. Write in standard form (biggest powers first): $2x^2 + 9x + 12$

Simplifying Polynomial Expressions

Step-by-step guide:

- ✓ In mathematics, a polynomial is an expression consisting of variables and coefficients that involves only the operations of addition, subtraction, multiplication, and non-negative integer exponents of variables.
  $$P(x) = a_n x^n + a_{n-1} x^{n-1} + \ldots + a_2 x^2 + a_1 x + a_0$$

Examples:

1) Simplify this Polynomial Expressions. $4x^2 - 5x^3 + 15x^4 - 12x^3 =$
   Combine "like" terms: $-5x^3 - 12x^3 = -17x^3$
   Then: $4x^2 - 5x^3 + 15x^4 - 12x^3 = 4x^2 - 17x^3 + 15x^4$
   Then write in standard form: $4x^2 - 17x^3 + 15x^4 = 15x^4 - 17x^3 + 4x^2$

2) Simplify this expression. $(2x^2 - x^4) - (4x^4 - x^2) =$
   First use distributive property: $\rightarrow$ multiply $(-)$ into $(4x^4 - x^2)$

$(2x^2 - x^4) - (4x^4 - x^2) = 2x^2 - x^4 - 4x^4 + x^2$

Then combine "like" terms: $2x^2 - x^4 - 4x^4 + x^2 = 3x^2 - 5x^4$

And write in standard form: $3x^2 - 5x^4 = -5x^4 + 3x^2$

The Distributive Property

Step-by-step guide:

- ✓ Distributive Property:
$$a(b + c) = ab + ac$$

Examples:

1) Simply. $(5x - 3)(-5) =$

   Use Distributive Property formula: $a(b + c) = ab + ac$

   $(5x - 3)(-5) = -25x + 15$

2) Simply $(-8)(2x - 8) =$

   Use Distributive Property formula: $a(b + c) = ab + ac$

   $(-8)(2x - 8) = -16x + 64$

Evaluating One Variable

Step-by-step guide:

- ✓ To evaluate one variable expression, find the variable and substitute a number for that variable.
- ✓ Perform the arithmetic operations.

Examples:

1) Solve this expression. $12 - 2x$, $x = -1$

   First substitute -1 for x, then:

   $12 - 2x = 12 - 2(-1) = 12 + 2 = 14$

2) Solve this expression. $-8 + 5x$, $x = 3$

   First substitute 3 for x, then:

$$-8 + 5x = -8 + 5(3) = -8 + 15 = 7$$

Evaluating Two Variables

Step-by-step guide:

- ✓ To evaluate an algebraic expression, substitute a number for each variable and perform the arithmetic operations.

Examples:

1) Solve this expression. $-3x + 5y$, $x = 2, y = -1$

First substitute 2 for x, and -1 for y , then:

$$-3x + 5y = -3(2) + 5(-1) = -6 - 5 = -11$$

2) Solve this expression. $2(a - 2b), a = -1, b = 3$

First substitute -1 for a, and 3 for b , then:

$$2(a - 2b) = 2a - 4b = 2(-1) - 4(3) = -2 - 12 = -14$$

Combining like Terms

Step-by-step guide:

- ✓ Terms are separated by "+" and "-" signs.
- ✓ Like terms are terms with same variables and same powers.
- ✓ Be sure to use the "+" or "-" that is in front of the coefficient.

Examples:

1) Simplify this expression. $(-5)(8x - 6) =$

Use Distributive Property formula: $a(b + c) = ab + ac$
$$(-5)(8x - 6) = -40x + 30$$

2) Simplify this expression. $(-3)(2x - 2) + 6 =$

First use Distributive Property formula: $a(b + c) = ab + ac$
$$(-3)(2x - 2) + 6 = -6x + 6 + 6$$

And Combining like Terms:

$-6x + 6 + 6 = -6x + 12$

One–Step Equations

Step-by-step guide:

✓ The values of two expressions on both sides of an equation are equal. $ax + b = c$
✓ You only need to perform one Math operation in order to solve the one-step equations.
✓ To solve one-step equation, find the inverse (opposite) operation is being performed.
✓ The inverse operations are:
  - Addition and subtraction
  - Multiplication and division

Examples:

1) Solve this equation. $x + 24 = 0 , x = ?$
   Here, the operation is addition and its inverse operation is subtraction. To solve this equation, subtract 24 from both sides of the equation: $x + 24 - 24 = 0 - 24$
   Then simplify: $x + 24 - 24 = 0 - 24 \rightarrow x = -24$

2) Solve this equation. $3x = 15, x = ?$
   Here, the operation is multiplication (variable x is multiplied by 3) and its inverse operation is division. To solve this equation, divide both sides of equation by 3:
   $$3x = 15 \rightarrow \frac{3x}{3} = \frac{15}{3} \rightarrow x = 5$$

Multi–Step Equations

Step-by-step guide:

✓ Combine "like" terms on one side.
✓ Bring variables to one side by adding or subtracting.
✓ Simplify using the inverse of addition or subtraction.
✓ Simplify further by using the inverse of multiplication or division.

Examples:

1) Solve this equation. $-(2 - x) = 5$

First use Distributive Property: $-(2-x) = -2+x$

Now solve by adding 2 to both sides of the equation. $-2+x = 5 \rightarrow -2+x+2 = 5+2$

Now simplify: $-2+x+2 = 5+2 \rightarrow x = 7$

2) Solve this equation. $4x+10 = 25-x$

First bring variables to one side by adding x to both sides.
$4x+10+x = 25-x+x \rightarrow 5x+10 = 25$. Now, subtract 10 from both sides:
$5x+10-10 = 25-10 \rightarrow 5x = 15$

Now, divide both sides by 5: $5x = 15 \rightarrow \frac{5x}{5} = \frac{15}{5} \rightarrow x = 3$

Graphing Single–Variable Inequalities

Step-by-step guide:

- ✓ Inequality is similar to equations and uses symbols for "less than" (<) and "greater than" (>).
- ✓ To solve inequalities, we need to isolate the variable. (like in equations)
- ✓ To graph an inequality, find the value of the inequality on the number line.
- ✓ For less than or greater than draw open circle on the value of the variable.
- ✓ If there is an equal sign too, then use filled circle.
- ✓ Draw a line to the right or to the left for greater or less than.

Examples:

1) Draw a graph for $x > 2$

Since, the variable is greater than 2, then we need to find 2 and draw an open circle above it. Then, draw a line to the right.

2) Graph this inequality. $x < 5$

One–Step Inequalities

Step-by-step guide:

- ✓ Similar to equations, first isolate the variable by using inverse operation.
- ✓ For dividing or multiplying both sides by negative numbers, flip the direction

of the inequality sign.

Examples:

Multi-Step Inequalities

1) Solve and graph the inequality. $x + 2 \geq 3$.

Subtract 2 from both sides. $x + 2 \geq 3 \rightarrow x + 2 - 2 \geq 3 - 2$, then: $x \geq 1$

2) Solve this inequality. $x - 1 \leq 2$

Add 1 to both sides. $x - 1 \leq 2 \rightarrow x - 1 + 1 \leq 2 + 1$, then: $x \leq 3$

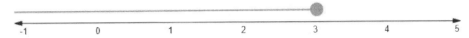

Step-by-step guide:

- ✓ Isolate the variable.
- ✓ Simplify using the inverse of addition or subtraction.
- ✓ Simplify further by using the inverse of multiplication or division.

Examples:

1) Solve this inequality. $2x - 2 \leq 6$

First add 2 to both sides: $2x - 2 + 2 \leq 6 + 2 \rightarrow 2x \leq 8$

Now, divide both sides by 2: $2x \leq 8 \rightarrow x \leq 4$

2) Solve this inequality. $2x - 4 \leq 8$

First add 4 to both sides: $2x - 4 + 4 \leq 8 + 4$

Then simplify: $2x - 4 + 4 \leq 8 + 4 \rightarrow 2x \leq 12$

Now divide both sides by 2: $\frac{2x}{2} \leq \frac{12}{2} \rightarrow x \leq 6$

Day 3 Practices

 Simplify each expression.

1) $(2x + x + 8 + 19) =$

2) $(-22x - 26x + 24) =$

3) $8x + 3 - 4x =$

4) $-2 - 5x^2 - 2x^2 =$

5) $3 + 10x^2 + 2 =$

6) $3x^2 + 6x + 12x^2 =$

 Simplify each polynomial.

7) $(2x^3 + 5x^2) - (12x + 2x^2) =$ _____

8) $(2x^5 + 2x^3) - (7x^3 + 6x^2) =$ _____

9) $(12x^4 + 4x^2) - (2x^2 - 6x^4) =$ _____

 Use the distributive property to simply each expression.

10) $2(2 + 3x) =$

11) $3(5 + 5x) =$

12) $4(3x - 8) =$

13) $(6x - 2)(-2) =$

14) $(-3)(x + 2) =$

15) $(2 + 2x)5 =$

 Evaluate each expression using the value given.

16) $5 + x, x = 2$

17) $x - 2, x = 4$

18) $8x + 1, x = 9$

19) $x - 12, x = -1$

20) $9 - x, x = 3$

21) $x + 2, x = 5$

 Evaluate each expression using the values given.

22) $2x + 4y, x = 3, y = 2$

23) $8x + 5y, x = 1, y = 5$

24) $-2a + 4b, a = 6, b = 3$

25) $4x + 7 - 2y, x = 7, y = 6$

✏️ Simplify each expression. (Combining like Terms)

26) $2x + x + 2 =$

27) $2(5x - 3) =$

28) $7x - 2x + 8 =$

29) $(-4)(3x - 5) =$

30) $9x - 7x - 5 =$

31) $16x - 5 + 8x =$

✏️ Solve each equation. (One–Step Equations)

32) $16 = -4 + x, x = $ ____

33) $x - 4 = -25, x = $ ____

34) $x + 12 = -9, x = $ ____

35) $14 = 18 - x, x = $ ____

36) $2 + x = -14, x = $ ____

37) $x - 5 = 15, x = $ ____

✏️ Solve each equation. (Multi–Step Equations)

38) $-3(2 + x) = 3$

39) $-2(4 + x) = 4$

40) $20 = -(x - 8)$

41) $2(2 - 2x) = 20$

42) $-12 = -(2x + 8)$

43) $5(2 + x) = 5$

✏️ Draw a graph for each inequality.

44) $x > -1$

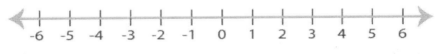

45) $x < 3$

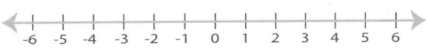

✏️ Solve each inequality and graph it.

46) $2x \geq 12$

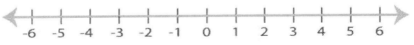

47) $4 + x \leq 5$

✏️ Solve each inequality.

48) $4x - 16 \leq 12$

49) $16x - 4 \leq 28$

50) $-15 + 9x \leq 30$

51) $2(x - 3) \leq 6$

52) $14x - 10 \leq 18$

53) $8x - 42 < 38$

Answers

1) $3x + 27$

2) $-48x + 24$

3) $4x + 3$

10) $6x + 4$

11) $15x + 15$

16) 7

17) 2

22) 14

23) 33

26) $3x + 2$

27) $10x - 6$

32) 20

33) -21

38) -3

39) -6

4) $-7x^2 - 2$

5) $10x^2 + 5$

6) $15x^2 + 6x$

12) $12x - 32$

13) $-12x + 4$

18) 73

19) -13

24) 0

25) 23

28) $5x + 8$

29) $-12x + 20$

34) -21

35) 4

40) -12

41) -4

7) $2x^3 + 3x^2 - 12x$

8) $2x^5 - 5x^3 - 6x^2$

9) $18x^4 + 2x^2$

14) $-3x - 6$

15) $10x + 10$

20) 6

21) 7

30) $2x - 5$

31) $24x - 5$

36) -16

37) 20

42) 2

43) -1

44)

45)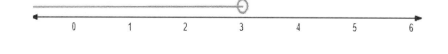

46)

47)

48) $x \le 7$

49) $x \le 2$

50) $x \le 5$

51) $x \le 6$

52) $x \le 2$

53) $x < 10$

Day 4:
Linear Equations and Inequalities

Math Topics that you'll learn today:

- ✓ Finding Slope
- ✓ Graphing Lines Using Slope–Intercept Form
- ✓ Graphing Lines Using Standard Form
- ✓ Writing Linear Equations
- ✓ Graphing Linear Inequalities
- ✓ Finding Midpoint
- ✓ Finding Distance of Two Points

"Nature is written in mathematical language." - Galileo Galilei

Finding Slope

Step-by-step guide:

- ✓ The slope of a line represents the direction of a line on the coordinate plane.
- ✓ A coordinate plane contains two perpendicular number lines. The horizontal line is x and the vertical line is y. The point at which the two axes intersect is called the origin. An ordered pair (x, y) shows the location of a point.
- ✓ A line on coordinate plane can be drawn by connecting two points.
- ✓ To find the slope of a line, we need two points.
- ✓ The slope of a line with two points A (x_1, y_1) and B (x_2, y_2) can be found by using this formula: $\frac{y_2 - y_1}{x_2 - x_1} = \frac{rise}{run}$

Examples:

1) Find the slope of the line through these two points: $(2, -10)$ *and* $(3, 6)$.

   Slope $= \frac{y_2 - y_1}{x_2 - x_1}$. Let (x_1, y_1) be $(2, -10)$ and (x_2, y_2) be $(3, 6)$. Then: slope $= \frac{y_2 - y_1}{x_2 - x_1} = \frac{6 - (-10)}{3 - 2} = \frac{6 + 10}{1} = \frac{16}{1} = 16$

2) Find the slope of the line containing two points $(8, 3)$ and $(-4, 9)$.

   Slope $= \frac{y_2 - y_1}{x_2 - x_1} \rightarrow (x_1, y_1) = (8, 3)$ and $(x_2, y_2) = (-4, 9)$. Then: slope $= \frac{y_2 - y_1}{x_2 - x_1} = \frac{9 - 3}{-4 - 8} = \frac{6}{-12} = \frac{1}{-2} = -\frac{1}{2}$

Graphing Lines Using Slope–Intercept Form

Step-by-step guide:

- ✓ Slope-intercept form of a line: given the slope m and the y-intercept (the intersection of the line and y-axis) b, then the equation of the line is:
$$y = mx + b$$

Example: *Sketch the graph of* $y = 8x - 3$.

To graph this line, we need to find two points. When x is zero the value of y is -3. And when y is zero the value of x is $\frac{3}{8}$. $x = 0 \rightarrow y = 8(0) - 3 = -3$, $y = 0 \rightarrow 0 = 8x - 3 \rightarrow x = \frac{3}{8}$

Now, we have two points: $(0, -3)$ and $(\frac{3}{8}, 0)$. Find the points and graph the line. Remember that the slope of the line is 8.

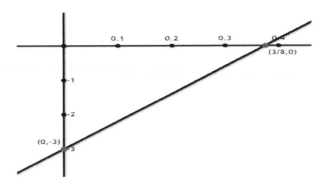

Graphing Lines Using Standard Form

Step-by-step guide:

- ✓ Find the $x-$intercept of the line by putting zero for y.
- ✓ Find the $y-$intercept of the line by putting zero for the x.
- ✓ Connect these two points.

Examples:

Sketch the graph of $x - y = -5$.

First isolate y for x: $x - y = -5 \rightarrow y = x + 5$
Find the x–intercept of the line by putting zero for y.
$y = x + 5 \rightarrow x + 5 = 0 \rightarrow x = -5$

Find the y–intercept of the line by putting zero for the x.
$y = 0 + 5 \rightarrow y = 5$

Then: x-intercept: $(-5, 0)$ and y-intercept: $(0, 5)$

Writing Linear Equations

Step-by-step guide:

- ✓ The equation of a line: $y = mx + b$
- ✓ Identify the slope.

✓ Find the y-intercept. This can be done by substituting the slope and the coordinates of a point (x, y) on the line.

Examples:

1) What is the equation of the line that passes through $(2, -2)$ and has a slope of 7?

The general slope-intercept form of the equation of a line is $y = mx + b$, where m is the slope and b is the y-intercept.

By substitution of the given point and given slope, we have: $-2 = (2)(7) + b$

So, $b = -2 - 14 = -16$, and the required equation is $y = 7x - 16$.

2) Write the equation of the line through $(2, 1)$ and $(-1, 4)$.

$Slop = \frac{y_2 - y_1}{x_2 - x_1} = \frac{4 - 1}{-1 - 2} = \frac{3}{-3} = -1 \rightarrow m = -1$

To find the value of b, you can use either points. The answer will be the same: $y = -x + b$

$(2, 1) \rightarrow 1 = -2 + b \rightarrow b = 3$

$(-1, 4) \rightarrow 4 = -(-1) + b \rightarrow b = 3$

The equation of the line is: $y = -x + 3$

Graphing Linear Inequalities

Step-by-step guide:

✓ First, graph the "equals" line.

✓ Choose a testing point. (it can be any point on both sides of the line.)

✓ Put the value of (x, y) of that point in the inequality. If that works, that part of the line is the solution. If the values don't work, then the other part of the line is the solution.

Examples:

Sketch the graph of $y < 2x - 3$. First, graph the line:

$y = 2x - 3$. The slope is 2 and y-intercept is -3. Then, choose a testing point. The easiest point to test is the origin: $(0, 0)$

$$(0,0) \rightarrow y < 2x - 3 \rightarrow 0 < 2(0) - 3 \rightarrow 0 < -3$$

0 is not less than -3. So, the other part of the line (on the right side) is the solution.

Finding Midpoint

Step-by-step guide:

- ✓ The middle of a line segment is its midpoint.
- ✓ The Midpoint of two endpoints A (x_1, y_1) and B (x_2, y_2) can be found using this formula: $M\left(\frac{x_1+x_2}{2}, \frac{y_1+y_2}{2}\right)$

Example:

1) Find the midpoint of the line segment with the given endpoints. $(4, -5), (0, 9)$

   Midpoint $= \left(\frac{x_1+x_2}{2}, \frac{y_1+y_2}{2}\right) \rightarrow (x_1, y_1) = (4, -5)$ and $(x_2, y_2) = (0, 9)$

   Midpoint $= \left(\frac{4+0}{2}, \frac{-5+9}{2}\right) \rightarrow \left(\frac{4}{2}, \frac{4}{2}\right) \rightarrow M(2, 2)$

2) Find the midpoint of the line segment with the given endpoints. $(6, 7), (4, -5)$

   Midpoint $= \left(\frac{x_1+x_2}{2}, \frac{y_1+y_2}{2}\right) \rightarrow (x_1, y_1) = (6, 7)$ and $(x_2, y_2) = (4, -5)$

   Midpoint $= \left(\frac{6+4}{2}, \frac{7-5}{2}\right) \rightarrow \left(\frac{10}{2}, \frac{2}{2}\right) \rightarrow (5, 1)$

Finding Distance of Two Points

Step-by-step guide:

- ✓ Distance of two points A (x_1, y_1) and B (x_2, y_2): $d = \sqrt{(x_1 - x_2)^2 + (y_1 - y_2)^2}$

Examples:

1) Find the distance between of $(0, 8), (-4, 5)$.

   Use distance of two points formula: $d = \sqrt{(x_1 - x_2)^2 + (y_1 - y_2)^2}$

   $(x_1, y_1) = (0, 8)$ and $(x_2, y_2) = (-4, 5)$. Then: $d = \sqrt{(x_1 - x_2)^2 + (y_1 - y_2)^2} \rightarrow$

$$d = \sqrt{(0 - (-4))^2 + (8 - 5)^2} = \sqrt{(4)^2 + (3)^2} = \sqrt{16 + 9} = \sqrt{25} = 5 \rightarrow d = 5$$

2) Find the distance of two points $(4, 2)$ and $(-5, -10)$.

Use distance of two points formula: $d = \sqrt{(x_1 - x_2)^2 + (y_1 - y_2)^2}$

$(x_1, y_1) = (4, 2)$, and $(x_2, y_2) = (-5, -10)$

Then: $d = \sqrt{(x_1 - x_2)^2 + (y_1 - y_2)^2} \rightarrow d = \sqrt{(4 - (-5))^2 + (2 - (-10))^2} =$

$\sqrt{(9)^2 + (12)^2} = \sqrt{81 + 144} = \sqrt{225} = 15$. Then: $d = 15$

Day 4 Practices

✍ *Find the slope of the line through each pair of points.*

1) $(1, 4), (3, 8)$

2) $(-1, 5), (0, 6)$

3) $(5, -5), (4, -1)$

4) $(-2, -1), (0, 5)$

5) $(5, 1), (2, 4)$

6) $(-3, 5), (-2, 8)$

✍ *Sketch the graph of each line. (Using Slope–Intercept Form)*

7) $y = \frac{1}{2}x - 4$

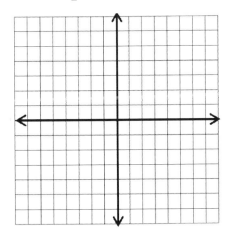

8) $y = 2x$

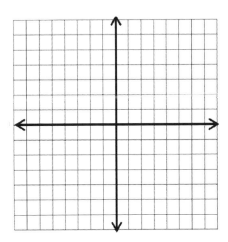

✍ *Sketch the graph of each line. (Graphing Lines Using Standard Form)*

9) $y = 3x - 2$

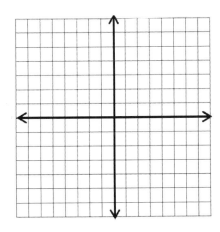

10) $y = -x + 1$

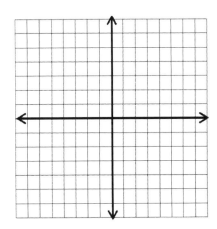

✍ **Write the equation of the line through the given points.**

11) through: $(1, -2), (-2, -17)$ 14) through: $(5, 4), (2, 1)$
12) through: $(-2, 1), (3, 6)$ 15) through: $(-4, 9), (3, 2)$
13) through: $(-2, 1), (0, 5)$ 16) through: $(1, 0), (5, 20)$

✍ **Sketch the graph of each linear inequality. (Graphing Linear Inequalities)**

17) $2y > 6x - 2$ 18) $3y < -3x + 12$

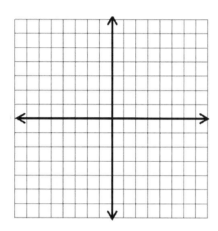   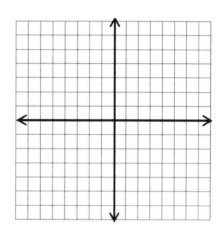

✍ **Find the midpoint of the line segment with the given endpoints.**

19) $(-4, -6), (2, 6)$ 22) $(-5, 2), (1, 6)$
20) $(7, 4), (-4, 1)$ 23) $(3, -2), (7, -6)$
21) $(-4, -1), (8, 3)$ 24) $(-7, -3), (5, -7)$

✍ **Find the distance between each pair of points.**

25) $(5, -1), (2, -5)$ 28) $(-1, -6), (4, 6)$
26) $(-4, -1), (0, 2)$ 29) $(3, -2), (-6, -14)$
27) $(-4, 2), (2, 10)$ 30) $(-3, 0), (1, 3)$

Answers

Find the slope of the line through each pair of points.

1) 2
2) 1

3) −4
4) 3

5) −1
6) 3

Sketch the graph of each line. (Using Slope–Intercept Form)

7)

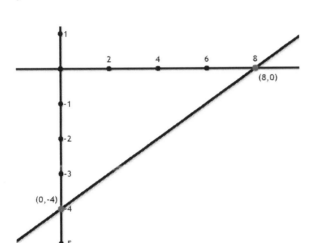

8)

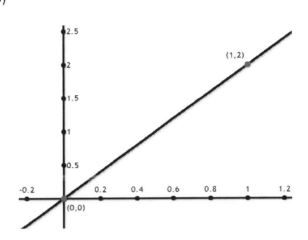

Sketch the graph of each line. (Graphing Lines Using Standard Form)

9) $y = 3x - 2$

10) $y = -x + 1$

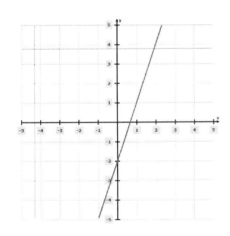

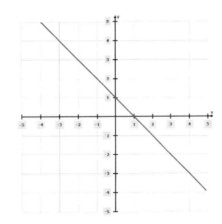

Write the equation of the line through the given points.

11) $y = 5x - 7$

12) $y = x + 3$

13) $y = 2x + 5$

14) $y = x - 1$

15) $y = -x + 5$

16) $y = 5x - 5$

Sketch the graph of each linear inequality. (Graphing Linear Inequalities)

17) $y > 3x - 1$

18) $y < -x + 4$

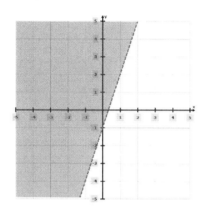 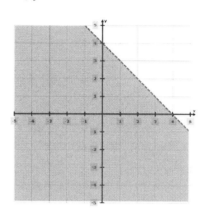

Find the midpoint of the line segment with the given endpoints.

19) $(-1, 0)$

20) $(1.5, 2.5)$

21) $(2, 1)$

22) $(-2, 4)$

23) $(5, -4)$

24) $(-1, -5)$

Find the distance between each pair of points.

25) 5

26) 5

27) 10

28) 13

29) 15

30) 5

Day 5:
Monomials and
Polynomials

Math Topics that you'll learn today:

- ✓ Writing Polynomials in Standard Form
- ✓ Simplifying Polynomials
- ✓ Adding and Subtracting Polynomials
- ✓ Multiplying Monomials
- ✓ Multiplying and Dividing Monomials
- ✓ Multiplying a Polynomial and a Monomial
- ✓ Multiplying Binomials
- ✓ Factoring Trinomials
- ✓ Operations with Polynomials

Mathematics is the supreme judge; from its decisions there is no appeal. – Tobias Dantzig

Simplifying Polynomials

Step-by-step guide:

✓ Find "like" terms. (they have same variables with same power).

✓ Use "FOIL". (First–Out–In–Last) for binomials:

$$(x + a)(x + b) = x^2 + (b + a)x + ab$$

✓ Add or Subtract "like" terms using order of operation.

Examples:

1) Simplify this expression. $4x(6x - 3) =$

Use Distributive Property: $4x(6x - 3) = 24x^2 - 12x$

2) Simplify this expression. $(6x - 2)(2x - 3) =$

First apply FOIL method: $(a + b)(c + d) = ac + ad + bc + bd$

$(6x - 2)(2x - 3) = 12x^2 - 18x - 4x + 6$

Now combine like terms: $12x^2 - 18x - 4x + 6 = 12x^2 - 22x + 6$

Adding and Subtracting Polynomials

Step-by-step guide:

✓ Adding polynomials is just a matter of combining like terms, with some order of operations considerations thrown in.

✓ Be careful with the minus signs, and don't confuse addition and multiplication!

Examples:

1) Simplify the expressions. $(4x^3 + 3x^4) - (x^4 - 5x^3) =$

First use Distributive Property for $-(x^4 - 5x^3)$, $\rightarrow -(x^4 - 5x^3) = -x^4 + 5x^3$

$(4x^3 + 3x^4) - (x^4 - 5x^3) = 4x^3 + 3x^4 - x^4 + 5x^3$

Now combine like terms: $4x^3 + 3x^4 - x^4 + 5x^3 = 2x^4 + 9x^3$

2) Add expressions. $(2x^3 - 6) + (9x^3 - 4x^2) =$

Remove parentheses: $(2x^3 - 6) + (9x^3 - 4x^2) = 2x^3 - 6 + 9x^3 - 4x^2$

Now combine like terms: $2x^3 - 6 + 9x^3 - 4x^2 = 11x^3 - 4x^2 - 6$

Multiplying Monomials

Step-by-step guide:

✓ A monomial is a polynomial with just one term, like $2x$ or $7y$.

Examples:

1) Multiply expressions. $5a^4b^3 \times 2a^3b^2 =$

Use this formula: $x^a \times x^b = x^{a+b}$

$a^4 \times a^3 = a^{4+3} = a^7$ and $b^3 \times b^2 = b^{3+2} = b^5$, Then: $5a^4b^3 \times 2a^3b^2 = 10a^7b^5$

2) Multiply expressions. $-4xy^4z^2 \times 3x^2y^5z^3 =$

Use this formula: $x^a \times x^b = x^{a+b} \rightarrow x \times x^2 = x^{1+2} = x^3$, $y^4 \times y^5 = y^{4+5} = y^9$

and $z^2 \times z^3 = z^{2+3} = z^5$, Then: $-4xy^4z^2 \times 3x^2y^5z^3 = -12x^3y^9z^5$

Multiplying and Dividing Monomials

Step-by-step guide:

✓ When you divide two monomials you need to divide their coefficients and then divide their variables.
✓ In case of exponents with the same base, you need to subtract their powers.
✓ Exponent's rules:

$$x^a \times x^b = x^{a+b}, \qquad \frac{x^a}{x^b} = x^{a-b}$$
$$\frac{1}{x^b} = x^{-b}, \quad (x^a)^b = x^{a \times b}$$
$$(xy)^a = x^a \times y^a$$

Examples:

1) Multiply expressions. $(-3x^7)(4x^3) =$
Use this formula: $x^a \times x^b = x^{a+b} \rightarrow x^7 \times x^3 = x^{10}$
Then: $(-3x^7)(4x^3) = -12x^{10}$

2) Dividing expressions. $\frac{18x^2y^5}{2xy^4} =$

Use this formula: $\frac{x^a}{x^b} = x^{a-b}$, $\frac{x^2}{x} = x^{2-1} = x$ and $\frac{y^5}{y^4} = y^{5-4} = y$

Then: $\frac{18x^2y^5}{2xy^4} = 9xy$

Multiplying a Polynomial and a Monomial

Step-by-step guide:

- ✓ When multiplying monomials, use the product rule for exponents.
- ✓ When multiplying a monomial by a polynomial, use the distributive property.

$$a \times (b + c) = a \times b + a \times c$$

Examples:

1) Multiply expressions. $-4x(5x + 9) =$

Use Distributive Property: $-4x(5x + 9) = -20x^2 - 36x$

2) Multiply expressions. $2x(6x^2 - 3y^2) =$

Use Distributive Property: $2x(6x^2 - 3y^2) = 12x^3 - 6xy^2$

Multiplying Binomials

Step-by-step guide:

- ✓ Use "FOIL". (First-Out-In-Last)
$$(x + a)(x + b) = x^2 + (b + a)x + ab$$

Examples:

1) Multiply Binomials. $(x - 2)(x + 2) =$

Use "FOIL". (First–Out–In–Last): $(x - 2)(x + 2) = x^2 + 2x - 2x - 4$

Then simplify: $x^2 + 2x - 2x - 4 = x^2 - 4$

2) Multiply Binomials. $(x + 5)(x - 2) =$

Use "FOIL". (First–Out–In–Last):

$(x + 5)(x - 2) = x^2 - 2x + 5x - 10$

Then simplify: $x^2 - 2x + 5x - 10 = x^2 + 3x - 10$

Factoring Trinomials

Step-by-step guide:

✓ "FOIL": $(x + a)(x + b) = x^2 + (b + a)x + ab$

✓ "Difference of Squares": $a^2 - b^2 = (a + b)(a - b)$

$$a^2 + 2ab + b^2 = (a + b)(a + b)$$
$$a^2 - 2ab + b^2 = (a - b)(a - b)$$

✓ "Reverse FOIL": $x^2 + (b + a)x + ab = (x + a)(x + b)$

Examples:

1) Factor this trinomial. $x^2 - 2x - 8 =$

Break the expression into groups: $(x^2 + 2x) + (-4x - 8)$

Now factor out x from $x^2 + 2x : x(x + 2)$ and factor out -4 from $-4x - 8: -4(x + 2)$

Then: $= x(x + 2) - 4(x + 2)$, now factor out like term: $x + 2$

Then: $(x + 2)(x - 4)$

2) Factor this trinomial. $x^2 - 6x + 8 =$

Break the expression into groups: $(x^2 - 2x) + (-4x + 8)$

Now factor out x from $x^2 - 2x : x(x - 2)$, and factor out -4 from $-4x + 8: -4(x - 2)$

Then: $= x(x - 2) - 4(x - 2)$, now factor out like term: $x - 2$

Then: $(x - 2)(x - 4)$

Operations with Polynomials

Step-by-step guide:

✓ When multiplying a monomial by a polynomial, use the distributive property.

$$a \times (b + c) = a \times b + a \times c = ab + ac$$

Examples:

1) Multiply. $5(2x - 6) =$

Use the distributive property: $5(2x - 6) = 10x - 30$

2) Multiply. $2x(6x + 2) =$

Use the distributive property: $2x(6 + 2) = 12x^2 + 4x$

Day 5 Practices

✎ *Simplify each polynomial.*

1) $5(2x - 10) =$

2) $2x(4x - 2) =$

3) $4x(5x - 3) =$

4) $3x(7x + 3) =$

5) $4x(8x - 4) =$

6) $5x(5x + 4) =$

✎ *Add or subtract polynomials.*

7) $(-x^2 - 2) + (2x^2 + 1) =$

8) $(2x^2 + 3) - (3 - 4x^2) =$

9) $(2x^3 + 3x^2) - (x^3 + 8) =$

10) $(4x^3 - x^2) + (3x^2 - 5x) =$

11) $(7x^3 + 9x) - (3x^3 + 2) =$

12) $(2x^3 - 2) + (2x^3 + 2) =$

✎ *Simplify each expression. (Multiplying Monomials)*

13) $4u^7 \times (-2u^5) =$

14) $(-2p^7) \times (-3p^2) =$

15) $3xy^2z^3 \times 2z^2 =$

16) $5u^5t \times 3ut^2 =$

17) $(-9a^6) \times (-5a^2b^4) =$

18) $-2a^3b^2 \times 4a^2b =$

✎ *Simplify each expression. (Multiplying and Dividing Monomials)*

19) $(3x^7y^2)(16x^5y^4) =$

20) $(4x^4y^6)(7x^3y^4) =$

21) $(7x^2y^9)(12x^9y^{12}) =$

22) $\frac{12x^6y^8}{4x^4y^2} =$

23) $\frac{52x^9y^5}{4x^3y^4} =$

24) $\frac{80x^{12}y^9}{10x^6y^7} =$

✎ **Find each product. (Multiplying a Polynomial and a Monomial)**

25) $3x(9x + 2y) =$

26) $6x(x + 2y) =$

27) $9x(2x + 4y) =$

28) $12x(3x + 9y) =$

29) $11x(2x - 11y) =$

30) $2x(6x - 6y) =$

✎ **Find each product. (Multiplying Binomials)**

31) $(x + 2)(x + 2) =$

32) $(x - 3)(x + 2) =$

33) $(x - 2)(x - 4) =$

34) $(x + 3)(x + 2) =$

35) $(x - 4)(x - 5) =$

36) $(x + 5)(x + 2) =$

✎ **Factor each trinomial.**

37) $x^2 + 8x + 15 =$

38) $x^2 - 5x + 6 =$

39) $x^2 + 6x + 8 =$

40) $x^2 - 8x + 16 =$

41) $x^2 - 7x + 12 =$

42) $x^2 + 11x + 18 =$

✎ **Find each product. (Operations with Polynomials)**

43) $9(6x + 2) =$

44) $8(3x + 7) =$

45) $5(6x - 1) =$

46) $-3(8x - 3) =$

47) $3x^2(6x - 5) =$

48) $5x^2(7x - 2) =$

Answers

1) $10x - 50$
2) $8x^2 - 4x$

3) $20x^2 - 12x$
4) $21x^2 + 9x$

5) $32x^2 - 16x$
6) $25x^2 + 20x$

7) $x^2 - 1$
8) $6x^2$
9) $x^3 + 3x^2 - 8$

10) $4x^3 + 2x^2 - 5x$
11) $4x^3 + 9x - 2$
12) $4x^3$

13) $-8u^{12}$
14) $6p^9$

15) $6xy^2z^5$
16) $15u^6t^3$

17) $45a^8b^4$
18) $-8a^5b^3$

19) $48x^{12}y^6$
20) $28x^7y^{10}$

21) $84x^{11}y^{21}$
22) $3x^2y^6$

23) $13x^6y$
24) $8x^6y^2$

25) $27x^2 + 6xy$
26) $6x^2 + 12xy$

27) $18x^2 + 36xy$
28) $36x^2 + 108xy$

29) $22x^2 - 121xy$
30) $12x^2 - 12xy$

31) $x^2 + 4x + 4$
32) $x^2 - x - 6$

33) $x^2 - 6x + 8$
34) $x^2 + 5x + 6$

35) $x^2 - 9x + 20$
36) $x^2 + 7x + 10$

37) $(x + 3)(x + 5)$
38) $(x - 2)(x - 3)$

39) $(x + 4)(x + 2)$
40) $(x - 4)(x - 4)$

41) $(x - 3)(x - 4)$
42) $(x + 2)(x + 9)$

43) $54x + 18$
44) $24x + 56$
45) $30x - 5$

46) $-24x + 9$
47) $18x^3 - 15x^2$

48) $35x^3 - 10x^2$

Day 6:
Geometry and Statistics

Math Topics that you'll learn today:

- ✓ The Pythagorean Theorem
- ✓ Triangles
- ✓ Polygons
- ✓ Circles
- ✓ Trapezoids
- ✓ Cubes
- ✓ Rectangle Prisms
- ✓ Cylinder
- ✓ Mean, Median, Mode, and Range of the Given Data
- ✓ Bar Graph
- ✓ Box and Whisker Plots
- ✓ Stem– And– Leaf Plot
- ✓ Pie Graph
- ✓ Probability

Mathematics is like checkers in being suitable for the young, not too difficult, amusing, and without peril to the state. – Plato

The Pythagorean Theorem

Step-by-step guide:

- ✓ In any right triangle: $a^2 + b^2 = c^2$

Examples:

1) Find the missing length.

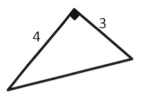

Use Pythagorean Theorem: $a^2 + b^2 = c^2$

Then: $a^2 + b^2 = c^2 \rightarrow 3^2 + 4^2 = c^2 \rightarrow 9 + 16 = c^2$

$c^2 = 25 \rightarrow c = 5$

2) Right triangle ABC has two legs of lengths 6 cm (AB) and 8 cm (AC). What is the length of the third side (BC)?

Use Pythagorean Theorem: $a^2 + b^2 = c^2$

Then: $a^2 + b^2 = c^2 \rightarrow 6^2 + 8^2 = c^2 \rightarrow 36 + 64 = c^2$

$c^2 = 100 \rightarrow c = 10$

Triangles

Step-by-step guide:

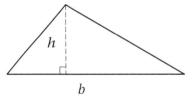

- ✓ In any triangle the sum of all angles is 180 degrees.
- ✓ Area of a triangle = $\frac{1}{2}$ ($base \times height$)
- ✓ All angles in a triangle sum up to 180 degrees.

Examples:

What is the area of triangles?

1)

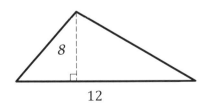

Solution:

Use the are formula: Area $= \frac{1}{2}$ ($base \times height$)

$base = 12$ and $height = 8$

Area $= \frac{1}{2}(12 \times 8) = \frac{1}{2}(96) = 48$

2)

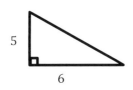

Solution:

Use the are formula: Area $= \frac{1}{2}(base \times height)$

$base = 6$ and $height = 5$

Area $= \frac{1}{2}(5 \times 6) = \frac{30}{2} = 15$

Polygons

Step-by-step guide:

Perimeter of a square $= 4 \times side = 4s$

s

Perimeter of a rectangle
$$= 2(width + length)$$

width

length

Perimeter of trapezoid
$$= a + b + c + d$$

a
d b
c

Perimeter of a regular hexagon $= 6a$

a

Example: Find the perimeter of following regular hexagon.

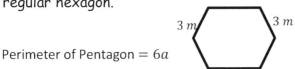
$3\ m$
$3\ m$ $3\ m$

Perimeter of Pentagon $= 6a$

Perimeter of Pentagon $= 6a = 6 \times 3 = 18m$

Perimeter of a parallelogram $= 2(l + w)$

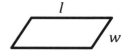
l
w

Circles

Step-by-step guide:

✓ In a circle, variable r is usually used for the radius and d for diameter and π is about 3.14.
✓ *Area of a circle $= \pi r^2$*
✓ *Circumference of a circle $= 2\pi r$*

Examples:

1) Find the area of the circle.
   Use area formula: *Area $= \pi r^2$* ,
   $r = 4$ then: *Area $= \pi(4)^2 = 16\pi$*, $\pi = 3.14$ then:
   $$Area = 16 \times 3.14 = 50.24$$

4 in

2) Find the Circumference of the circle.

Use Circumference formula: $Circumference = 2\pi r$

$r = 6$, then: $Circumference = 2\pi(6) = 12\pi$

$\pi = 3.14$ then: $Circumference = 12 \times 3.14 = 37.68$

$$(\pi = 3.14)$$

Trapezoids

Step-by-step guide:

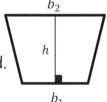

- ✓ A quadrilateral with at least one pair of parallel sides is a trapezoid.
- ✓ Area of a trapezoid $= \frac{1}{2}h(b_1 + b_2)$

Example:

Calculate the area of the trapezoid.

Use area formula: $A = \frac{1}{2}h(b_1 + b_2)$

$b_1 - 12$, $b_2 - 16$ and $h = 18$

Then: $A = \frac{1}{2}18(12 + 16) = 9(28) = 252\ cm^2$

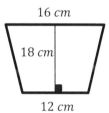

Cubes

Step-by-step guide:

- ✓ A cube is a three-dimensional solid object bounded by six square sides.
- ✓ Volume is the measure of the amount of space inside of a solid figure, like a cube, ball, cylinder or pyramid.
- ✓ Volume of a cube $= (one\ side)^3$
- ✓ surface area of cube $= 6 \times (one\ side)^2$

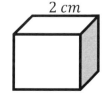

Example:

Find the volume and surface area of this cube.

Use volume formula: $volume = (one\ side)^3$

Then: $volume = (one\ side)^3 = (2)^3 = 8\ cm^3$

Use surface area formula: $surface\ area\ of\ cube: 6(one\ side)^2 = 6(2)^2 = 6(4) = 24\ cm^2$

Rectangular Prisms

Step-by-step guide:

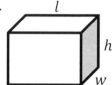

- ✓ A solid 3-dimensional object which has six rectangular faces.
- ✓ Volume of a Rectangular prism = **Length × Width × Height**

$Volume = l \times w \times h$ $Surface\ area = 2(wh + lw + lh)$

Example:

Find the volume and surface area of rectangular prism.

Use volume formula: $Volume = l \times w \times h$

Then: $Volume = 10 \times 5 \times 8 = 400\ m^3$

Use surface area formula: $Surface\ area = 2(wh + lw + lh)$

Then: $Surface\ area = 2(5 \times 8 + 10 \times 5 + 10 \times 8) = 2(40 + 50 + 80) = 340\ m^2$

Cylinder

Step-by-step guide:

- ✓ A cylinder is a solid geometric figure with straight parallel sides and a circular or oval cross section.
- ✓ $Volume\ of\ Cylinder\ Formula = \pi\ (radius)^2 \times height$,$(\pi = 3.14)$
- ✓ $Surface\ area\ of\ a\ cylinder = 2\pi r^2 + 2\pi rh$

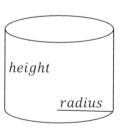

Example:

Find the volume and Surface area of the follow Cylinder.

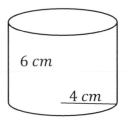

Use volume formula: $Volume = \pi(radius)^2 \times height$
Then: $Volume = \pi(4)^2 \times 6 = \pi 16 \times 6 = 96\pi$
$\pi = 3.14$ then: $Volume = 96\pi = 301.44$
Use surface area formula: $Surface\ area = 2\pi r^2 + 2\pi rh$
Then: $= 2\pi(4)^2 + 2\pi(4)(6) = 2\pi(16) + 2\pi(24) = 32\pi + 48\pi = 80\pi$
$\pi = 3.14$ then: $Surface\ area = 80 \times 3.14 = 251.2$

Mean, Median, Mode, and Range of the Given Data

Step-by-step guide:

- ✓ Mean: $\dfrac{\text{sum of the data}}{\text{total number of data entires}}$
- ✓ Mode: value in the list that appears most often
- ✓ Range: the difference of largest value and smallest value in the list

Examples:

1) What is the median of these numbers? $4, 9, 13, 8, 15, 18, 5$

   Write the numbers in order: $4, 5, 8, 9, 13, 15, 18$

   Median is the number in the middle. Therefore, the median is 9.

2) What is the mode of these numbers? $22, 16, 12, 9, 7, 6, 4, 6$

   Mode: value in the list that appears most often
   Therefore: mode is 6

Pie Graph

Step-by-step guide:

- ✓ A Pie Chart is a circle chart divided into sectors; each sector represents the relative size of each value.

Example:

A library has 840 books that include Mathematics, Physics, Chemistry, English and History. Use following graph to answer question.

What is the number of Mathematics books?

Number of total books $= 840$,
Percent of Mathematics books $= 30\% = 0.30$
Then: $0.30 \times 840 = 252$

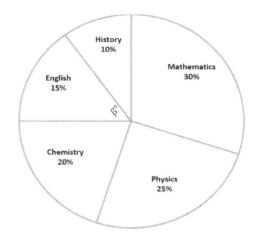

Probability Problems

Step-by-step guide:

✓ Probability is the likelihood of something happening in the future. It is expressed as a number between zero (can never happen) to 1 (will always happen).
✓ Probability can be expressed as a fraction, a decimal, or a percent.

Examples:

1) If there are 8 red balls and 12 blue balls in a basket, what is the probability that John will pick out a red ball from the basket?

   There are 8 red ball and 20 are total number of balls. Therefore, probability that John will pick out a red ball from the basket is 8 out of 20 or $\frac{8}{8+12} = \frac{8}{20} = \frac{2}{5}$.

2) A bag contains 18 balls: two green, five black, eight blue, a brown, a red and one white. If 17 balls are removed from the bag at random, what is the probability that a brown ball has been removed?

   If 17 balls are removed from the bag at random, there will be one ball in the bag.

   The probability of choosing a brown ball is 1 out of 18. Therefore, the probability of not choosing a brown ball is 17 out of 18 and the probability of having not a brown ball after removing 17 balls is the same.

Day 6 Practices

✎ *Find the missing side?*

1)   2)   3)   4)

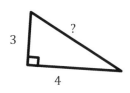   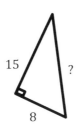   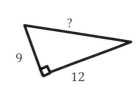   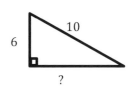

✎ *Find the measure of the unknown angle in each triangle.*

5)   6)   7)   8)

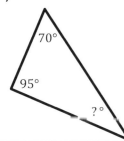   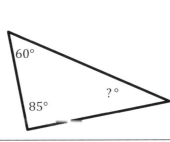   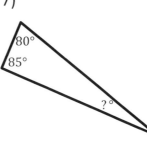   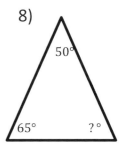

✎ *Find the perimeter of each shape.*

9)   10)   11)   12)

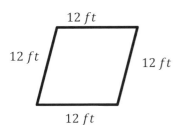   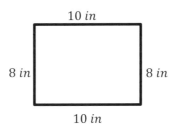   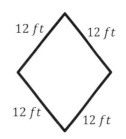   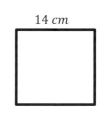

✎ **Complete the table below.** ($\pi = 3.14$)

13)

	Radius	Diameter	Circumference	Area
Circle 1	4 inches	8 inches	25.12 inches	50.24 square inches
Circle 2		12 meters		
Circle 3				12.56 square ft
Circle 4			18.84 miles	

✎ **Find the area of each trapezoid.**

14)

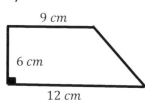

9 cm

6 cm

12 cm

15)

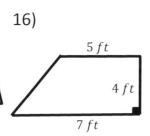

14 m

10 m

18 m

16)

5 ft

4 ft

7 ft

17)

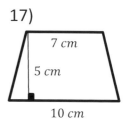

7 cm

5 cm

10 cm

✎ **Find the volume of each cube.**

18)

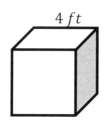

4 ft

19)

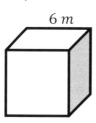

6 m

20)

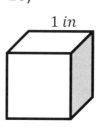

1 in

21)

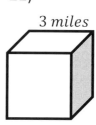

3 miles

✎ **Find the volume of each Rectangular Prism.**

22)

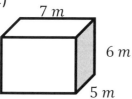

7 m

6 m

5 m

23)

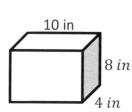

10 in

8 in

4 in

24)

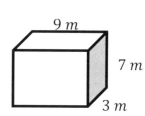

9 m

7 m

3 m

✎ **Find the volume of each Cylinder. Round your answer to the nearest tenth.** (π = 3.14)

25)

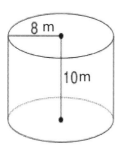

8 m

10m

26)

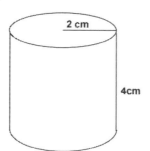

2 cm

4cm

27)

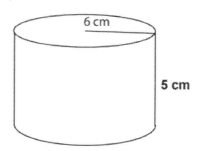

6 cm

5 cm

✎ *Solve.*

28) In a javelin throw competition, five athletics score 56, 58, 63, 57 and 61 meters. What are their Mean and Median? _____

✎ The circle graph below shows all Jason's expenses for last month. Jason spent $300 on his bills last month.

29) How much did Jason spend on his car last month? _____

30) How much did Jason spend for foods last month? _____

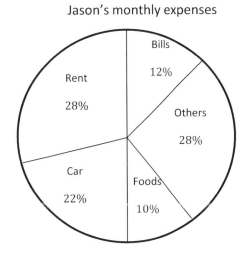

Jason's monthly expenses

Solve.

31) Bag A contains 9 red marbles and 3 green marbles. Bag B contains 9 black marbles and 6 orange marbles. What is the probability of selecting a green marble at random from bag A? What is the probability of selecting a black marble at random from Bag B? _____ _____

Answers

1) 5
2) 17
3) 15
4) 8

5) 15°
6) 35°
7) 15°
8) 65°

9) 48 ft
10) 36 in
11) 48 ft
12) 56 cm

13)

	Radius	Diameter	Circumference	Area
Circle 1	4 *inches*	8 *inches*	25.12 *inches*	50.24 *square inches*
Circle 2	6 *meters*	12 *meters*	37.68 *meters*	113.04 *square meters*
Circle 3	2 *ft*	4 *ft*	12.56 *ft*	12.56 *square ft*
Circle 4	3 *miles*	6 *miles*	18.84 *miles*	28.26 *square miles*

14) 63 cm^2
15) 160 m^2
16) 24 ft^2
17) 42.5 cm^2

18) 64 ft^3
19) 216 m^3
20) 1 in^3
21) 27 $miles^3$

22) 210 m^3
23) 320 in^3
24) 189 m^3

25) 2,009.6 m^3
26) 50.2 cm^3
27) 565.2 cm^3

28) *Mean*: 59, *Median*: 58
29) $550
30) $250

31) $\frac{1}{4}, \frac{3}{5}$

Day 7:
Geometry and Statistics

Math Topics that you'll learn today:

- ✓ Systems of Equations
- ✓ Quadratic Equation
- ✓ Graphing Quadratic Functions
- ✓ Quadratic Inequalities
- ✓ Graphing Quadratic inequalities
- ✓ Adding and subtracting complex numbers
- ✓ Multiplying and dividing complex numbers
- ✓ Rationalizing Imaginary Denominators
- ✓ Function Notation
- ✓ Adding and Subtracting Functions
- ✓ Multiplying and Dividing Functions
- ✓ Composition of Functions
- ✓ Trig Ratios of General Angles
- ✓ Angles and Angle Measure
- ✓ Evaluating Trigonometric Function

Systems of Equations

Step-by-step guide:

- ✓ A system of equations contains two equations and two variables. For example, consider the system of equations: $x - y = 1, x + y = 5$
- ✓ The easiest way to solve a system of equation is using the elimination method. The elimination method uses the addition property of equality. You can add the same value to each side of an equation.
- ✓ For the first equation above, you can add $x + y$ to the left side and 5 to the right side of the first equation: $x - y + (x + y) = 1 + 5$. Now, if you simplify, you get: $x - y + (x + y) = 1 + 5 \rightarrow 2x = 6 \rightarrow x = 3$. Now, substitute 3 for the x in the first equation: $3 - y = 1$. By solving this equation, $y = 2$

Example:

What is the value of $x + y$ in this system of equations? $\begin{cases} 3x - 4y = -20 \\ -x + 2y = 10 \end{cases}$

Solving Systems of Equations by Elimination: $\begin{array}{c} 3x - 4y = -20 \\ -x + 2y = 10 \end{array}$ $\Rightarrow$ Multiply the second equation by 3, then add it to the first equation.

$\begin{array}{l} 3x - 4y = -20 \\ 3(-x + 2y = 10) \end{array} \Rightarrow \begin{array}{l} 3x - 4y = -20 \\ -3x + 6y = 30 \end{array} \Rightarrow 2y = 10 \Rightarrow y = 5$. Now, substitute 5 for y in the first equation and solve for x. $3x - 4(5) = -20 \rightarrow 3x - 20 = -20 \rightarrow x = 0$

Quadratic Equation

Step-by-step guide:

- ✓ Write the equation in the form of: $ax^2 + bx + c = 0$
- ✓ Factorize the quadratic and solve for the variable.
- ✓ Use quadratic formula if you couldn't factorize the quadratic.
- ✓ Quadratic formula: $x = \frac{-b \pm \sqrt{b^2 - 4ac}}{2a}$

Examples:

Find the solutions of each quadratic.

1) $x^2 + 5x - 6 = 0$

Use quadratic formula: $= \dfrac{-b \pm \sqrt{b^2 - 4ac}}{2a}$, $a = 1, b = 5$ and $c = -6$

then: $x = \dfrac{-5 \pm \sqrt{5^2 - 4.1(-6)}}{2(1)}$, $x_1 = \dfrac{-5 + \sqrt{5^2 - 4 \times 1(-6)}}{2(1)} = 1$, $x_2 = \dfrac{-5 - \sqrt{5^2 - 4 \times 1(-6)}}{2(1)} = -6$

2) $x^2 + 6x + 8 = 0$

Use quadratic formula: $= \dfrac{-b \pm \sqrt{b^2 - 4ac}}{2a}$, $a = 1, b = 6$ and $c = 8$

$x = \dfrac{-6 \pm \sqrt{6^2 - 4.1.8}}{2.1}$, $x_1 = \dfrac{-6 + \sqrt{6^2 - 4.1.8}}{2.1} = -2$, $x_2 = \dfrac{-6 - \sqrt{6^2 - 4.1.8}}{2.1} = -4$

Graphing Quadratic Functions

Step-by-step guide:

- ✓ Quadratic functions in vertex form: $y = a(x - h)^2 + k$ where (h, k) is the vertex of the function. The axis of symmetry is $x = h$
- ✓ Quadratic functions in standard form: $y = ax^2 + bx + c$ where $x = -\dfrac{b}{2a}$ is the value of x in the vertex of the function.
- ✓ To graph a quadratic function, first find the vertex, then substitute some values for x and solve for y.

Example:

Sketch the graph of $y = 3(x + 1)^2 + 2$.

The vertex of $3(x + 1)^2 + 2$ *is* $(-1, 2)$. Substitute zero for x and solve for y. $y = 3(0 + 1)^2 + 2 = 5$. The y Intercept is $(0, 5)$.

Now, you can simply graph the quadratic function.

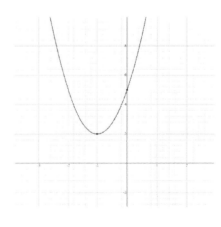

Quadratic Inequalities

Step-by-step guide:

- ✓ A quadratic inequality is one that can be written in one of the following standard forms:

$$ax^2 + bx + c > 0, \ ax^2 + bx + c < 0, \ ax^2 + bx + c \geq 0, \ ax^2 + bx + c \leq 0$$

- ✓ Solving a quadratic inequality is like solving equations. We need to find the solutions.

Examples:

1) **Solve quadratic inequality.** $-x^2 - 5x + 6 > 0$

   Factor: $-x^2 - 5x + 6 > 0 \rightarrow -(x - 1)(x + 6) > 0$

   Multiply both sides by -1: $\left(-(x-1)(x+6)\right)(-1) > 0(-1) \rightarrow (x-1)(x+6) < 0$

   Then the solution could be $-6 < x < 1$ or $-6 > x$ and $x > 1$. Choose a value between -1 and 6 and check. Let's try 0. Then: $-0^2 - 5(0) + 6 > 0 \rightarrow 6 > 0$. This is true! So, the answer is: $-6 < x < 1$

2) **Solve quadratic inequality.** $x^2 - 3x - 10 \geq 0$

   Factor: $x^2 - 3x - 10 \geq 0 \rightarrow (x + 2)(x - 5) \geq 0$. -2 and 5 are the solutions. Now, the solution could be $-2 \leq x \leq 5$ or $-6 \geq x$ and $x \geq 1$. Let's choose zero to check:

   $0^2 - 3(0) - 10 \geq 0 \rightarrow -10 \geq 0$, which is not true. So, $-6 \geq x$ and $x \geq 1$

Graphing Quadratic Inequalities

Step-by-step guide:

- ✓ A quadratic inequality is in the form $y > ax^2 + bx + c$ (or substitute $<, \leq,$ or $\geq$ for $>$).
- ✓ To graph a quadratic inequality, start by graphing the quadratic parabola. Then fill in the region either inside or outside of it, depending on the inequality.
- ✓ Choose a testing point and check the solution section.

Example: *Sketch the graph of* $y > 2x^2$.

First, graph $y = 2x^2$

Since, the inequality sing is $>$, we need to use dash lines.

Now, choose a testing point inside the parabola. Let's choose $(0,2)$. $y > 2x^2 \rightarrow 2 > 2(0)^2 \rightarrow 2 > 0$

This is true. So, inside the parabola is the solution section.

Adding and Subtracting Complex Numbers

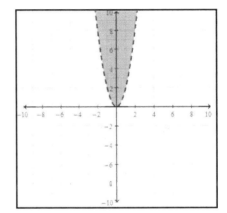

Step-by-step guide:

- ✓ A complex number is expressed in the form $a + bi$, where a and b are real numbers, and i, which is called an imaginary number, is a solution of the equation $x^2 = -1$
- ✓ For adding complex numbers: $(a + bi) + (c + di) = (a + c) + (b + d)i$
- ✓ For subtracting complex numbers: $(a + bi) - (c + di) = (a - c) + (b - d)i$

Examples:

1) Solve: $-8 + (2i) + (-8 + 6i)$

   Remove parentheses: $-8 + (2i) + (-8 + 6i) \rightarrow -8 + 2i - 8 + 6i$

   Group like terms: $-8 + 2i - 8 + 6i \rightarrow -8 - 8 + 2i + 6i$

   Add similar terms: $-8 - 8 + 2i + 6i = -16 + 8i$

2) Solve: $-2 + (-8 - 7i) - 9$

   Remove parentheses: $-2 + (-8 - 7i) - 9 \rightarrow -2 - 8 - 7i - 9$

   Combine like terms: $2 - 8 - 7i - 9 = -19 - 7i$

Multiplying and Dividing Complex Numbers

Step-by-step guide:

- ✓ Multiplying complex numbers: $(a + bi) + (c + di) = (ac - bd) + (ad + bc)i$
- ✓ Dividing complex numbers: $\dfrac{a+bi}{c+di} = \dfrac{a+bi}{c+di} \times \dfrac{c-di}{c-di} = \dfrac{ac+bd}{c^2-d^2} + \dfrac{bc-ad}{c^2-d^2} i$
- ✓ Imaginary number rule: $i^2 = -1$

Examples:

1) Solve: $(2 - 8i)(3 - 5i)$

   Use the rule: $(a - bi) + (c + di) = (ac - bd) + (ad + bc)i$

   $(2.3 - (-8) - 5)) + (2(-5) + (-8).3)i = -34 - 34i$

2) Solve: $\dfrac{2-3i}{2+i} =$

   Use the rule for dividing complex numbers:
   $$\dfrac{a + bi}{c + di} = \dfrac{a + bi}{c + di} \times \dfrac{c - di}{c - di} = \dfrac{ac + bd}{c^2 - d^2} + \dfrac{bc - ad}{c^2 - d^2} i \rightarrow$$
   $$\dfrac{2 - 3i}{2 + i} \times \dfrac{2 - i}{2 - i} = \dfrac{2 \times (2) + (-3)(1)}{2^2 - (i)^2} + \dfrac{(-3) \times (2) - (2)(1)}{2^2 - (-1)} i = \dfrac{1}{5} - \dfrac{8}{5} i$$

Rationalizing Imaginary Denominators

Step-by-step guide:

- ✓ Step 1: Find the conjugate (it's the denominator with different sign between the two terms.
- ✓ Step 2: Multiply numerator and denominator by the conjugate.
- ✓ Step 3: Simplify if needed.

Examples:

1) Solve: $\dfrac{5i}{2 - 3i}$

Multiply by the conjugate: $\frac{2+3i}{2+3i} \rightarrow \frac{5i(2+3i)}{(2-3i)(2+3i)} = \frac{15i^2+10i}{(2-3i)(2+3i)} = \frac{-15+10i}{(2-3i)(2+3i)}$

Use complex arithmetic rule: $(a+bi)(a-bi) = a^2 + b^2$

$(2-3i)(2+3i) = 2^2 + (-3)^2 = 13$, Then: $\frac{-15+10i}{(2-3i)(2+3i)} = \frac{-15+10i}{13}$

2) Solve: $\frac{4-9i}{-6i}$

Apply fraction rule: $\frac{4-9i}{-6i} = -\frac{4-9i}{6i}$

Multiply by the conjugate: $\frac{-i}{-i}$. $\quad -\frac{4-9i}{6i} = -\frac{(4-9i)(-i)}{6i(-i)} = -\frac{-9-4i}{6}$

Function Notation

Step-by-step guide:

- ✓ Functions are mathematical operations that assign unique outputs to given inputs.
- ✓ Function notation is the way a function is written. It is meant to be a precise way of giving information about the function without a rather lengthy written explanation.
- ✓ The most popular function notation is $f(x)$ which is read "f of x".

Examples:

1) Evaluate: $w(x) = 3x + 1$, find $w(4)$. Substitute x with 4: Then: $w(x) = 3x + 1 \rightarrow w(4) = 3(4) + 1 \rightarrow w(x) = 12 + 1 \rightarrow w(x) = 13$

2) Evaluate: $h(n) = n^2 - 10$, find $h(-2)$. Substitute x with -2:

Then: $h(n) = n^2 - 10 \rightarrow h(-2) = (-2)^2 - 10 \rightarrow h(-2) = 4 - 10 \rightarrow h(-2) = -6$

Adding and Subtracting Functions

Step-by-step guide:

- ✓ Just like we can add and subtract numbers, we can add and subtract functions. For example, if we had functions f and g, we could create two new functions:
- ✓ f + g and f - g.

Examples:

1) $f(x) = 2x + 4$, $g(x) = x + 3$, Find: $(f - g)(1)$

$(f - g)(x) = f(x) - g(x)$, then: $(f - g)(x) = 2x + 4 - (x + 3)$

$= 2x + 4 - x - 3 = x + 1$

Substitute x with 1: $(f - g)(1) = 1 + 1 = 2$

2) $g(a) = 2a - 1$, $f(a) = -a - 4$, Find: $(g + f)(-1)$

$(g + f)(a) = g(a) + f(a)$, Then: $(g + f)(a) = 2a - 1 - a - 4 = a - 5$

Substitute a with -1: $(g + f)(a) = a - 5 = -1 - 5 = -6$

Multiplying and Dividing Functions

Step-by-step guide:

- ✓ Just like we can multiply and divide numbers, we can multiply and divide functions. For example, if we had functions f and g, we could create two new functions: f × g, and $\frac{f}{g}$.

Examples:

1) $g(x) = -x - 2$, $f(x) = 2x + 1$, Find: $(g.f)(2)$

$(g.f)(x) = g(x).f(x) = (-x - 2)(2x + 1) = -2x^2 - x - 4x - 2 = -2x^2 - 5x - 2$

Substitute x with 2:

$(g.f)(x) = -2x^2 - 5x - 2 = -2(2)^2 - 5(2) - 2 = -8 - 10 - 2 = -20$

2) $f(x) = x + 4$, $h(x) = 5x - 2$, Find: $\left(\frac{f}{h}\right)(-1)$

$\left(\frac{f}{h}\right)(x) = \frac{f(x)}{h(x)} = \frac{x+4}{5x-2}$

Substitute x with -1: $\left(\frac{f}{h}\right)(x) = \frac{x+4}{5x-2} = \frac{(-1)+4}{5(-1)-2} = \frac{3}{-7} = -\frac{3}{7}$

Composition of Functions

Step-by-step guide:

- ✓ The term "composition of functions" (or "composite function") refers to the combining together of two or more functions in a manner where the output from one function becomes the input for the next function.
- ✓ The notation used for composition is: $(f \circ g)(x) = f(g(x))$

Examples:

1) *Using $f(x) = x + 2$ and $g(x) = 4x$, find: $f(g(1))$*

$(f \circ g)(x) = f(g(x))$

Then: $(f \circ g)(x) = f\big(g(x)\big) = f(4x) = 4x + 2$

Substitute x with 1: $(f \circ g)(1) = 4 + 2 = 6$

2) *Using $f(x) = 5x + 4$ and $g(x) = x - 3$, find: $g(f(3))$*

$(f \circ g)(x) = f(g(x))$

Then: $(g \circ f)(x) = g\big(f(x)\big) = g(5x + 4)$, *now substitute x in $g(x)$ by $5x + 4$.*

Then: $g(5x + 4) = (5x + 4) - 3 = 5x + 4 - 3 = 5x + 1$

Substitute x with 3: $(g \circ f)(x) = g\big(f(x)\big) = 5x + 1 = 5(3) + 1 = 15 = 1 = 16$

Trig Ratios of General Angles

Step-by-step guide:

✓ Learn common trigonometric functions:

θ	0°	30°	45°	60°	90°
$\sin \theta$	0	$\frac{1}{2}$	$\frac{\sqrt{2}}{2}$	$\frac{\sqrt{3}}{2}$	1
$\cos \theta$	1	$\frac{\sqrt{3}}{2}$	$\frac{\sqrt{2}}{2}$	$\frac{1}{2}$	0
$\tan \theta$	0	$\frac{\sqrt{3}}{3}$	1	$\sqrt{3}$	Undefined

Examples:

Find each trigonometric function.

1) $sin - 120°$. Use the following property: $sin(-x) = -sin(x)$

$sin - 120° = -sin\ 120°$. $sin\ 120° = \frac{\sqrt{3}}{2}$, then: $sin - 120° = -\frac{\sqrt{3}}{2}$

2) $cos\ 150°$

Recall that $cos\ 150° = -cos\ 30°$. Then: $cos\ 150° = -cos\ 30° = -\frac{\sqrt{3}}{2}$

Angles and Angle Measure

Step-by-step guide:

✓ To convert degrees to radians, use this formula: $\boldsymbol{Radians = Degrees \times \frac{\pi}{180}}$
✓ To convert radians to degrees, use this formula: $\boldsymbol{Degrees = Radians \times \frac{180}{\pi}}$

Examples:

1) Convert 150 degrees to radians.

Use this formula: $Radians = Degrees \times \frac{\pi}{180}$

$$Radians = 150 \times \frac{\pi}{180} = \frac{150\pi}{180} = \frac{5\pi}{6}$$

2) Convert $\frac{2\pi}{3}$ to degrees.

Use this formula: $Degrees = Radians \times \frac{180}{\pi}$

$$Degrees = \frac{2\pi}{3} \times \frac{180}{\pi} = \frac{360\pi}{3\pi} = 120°$$

Evaluating Trigonometric Function

Step-by-step guide:

- ✓ Step 1: Draw the terminal side of the angle.

- ✓ Step 2: Find reference angle. (It is the smallest angle that you can make from the terminal side of an angle with the x-axis.)

- ✓ Step 3: Find the trigonometric function of the reference angle.

Examples:

1) *Find the exact value of trigonometric function.* $cos\ 225°$

   Write $cos\ (225°)$ as $cos\ (180° + 45°)$. Recall that $cos\ 180° = -1, cos\ 45° = \frac{\sqrt{2}}{2}$

   $225°$ is in the third quadrant and cosine is negative in the quadrant 3. *The reference angle of* $225°$ is $45°$. Therefore, $cos\ 225° = -\frac{\sqrt{2}}{2}$

2) *Find the exact value of trigonometric function.* $tan\ \frac{7\pi}{6}$

   Rewrite the angles for $tan\ \frac{7\pi}{6}$:

   $$tan\ \frac{7\pi}{6} = tan\ \left(\frac{6\pi+\pi}{6}\right) = tan(\pi + \frac{1}{6}\pi)$$

   Use the periodicity of tan: $tan(x + \pi.k) = tan(x)$

   $$tan\left(\pi + \frac{1}{6}\pi\right) = tan\left(\frac{1}{6}\pi\right) = \frac{\sqrt{3}}{3}$$

Day 7 Practices

✍ *Solve each system of equations.*

1) $-5x + y = -3$ $x = $ ___
   $3x - 8y = 24$ $y = $ ___

2) $3x - 2y = 2$ $x = $ ___
   $5x - 5y = 10$ $y = $ ___

3) $8x + 14y = 4$ $x = $ ___
   $-6x - 7y = -10$ $y = $ ___

4) $10x + 7y = 1$ $x = $ ___
   $-5x - 7y = 24$ $y = $ ___

✍ *Factor each expression.*

5) $x^2 - 5x + 4 = $

6) $x^2 + 6x + 8 = $

7) $x^2 + x - 12 = $

8) $x^2 - 7x + 10 = $

9) $x^2 - 4x - 12 = $

10) $2x^2 - 3x - 2 = $

✍ *Solve each quadratic inequality.*

11) $x^2 + 4x - 5 > 0$

12) $x^2 - 2x - 3 \geq 0$

13) $x^2 - 1 < 0$

14) $17x^2 + 15x - 2 \geq 0$

15) $4x^2 + 20x - 11 < 0$

16) $12x^2 + 10x - 12 > 0$

✍ *Simplify.*

17) $(-3 + 6i) - (-9 - i) = $

18) $(-5 + 15i) - (-3 + 3i) = $

19) $(-14 + i) - (-12 - 11i) = $

20) $(-18 - 3i) + (11 + 5i) = $

21) $(-11 - 9i) - (-9 - 3i) = $

22) $-8 + (2i) + (-8 + 6i) = $

✍ *Simplify.*

23) $(-2 - i)(4 + i) = $

24) $(2 - 2i)^2 = $

25) $(4 - 3i)(6 - 6i) = $

26) $\dfrac{-1 + 5i}{-8 - 7i} = $

27) $\dfrac{-2 - 9i}{-2 + 7i} = $

28) $\dfrac{4 + i}{2 - 5i} = $

✍ *Simplify.*

29) $\dfrac{-2}{-2i} = $

30) $\dfrac{-1}{-9i} = $

31) $\dfrac{-8}{-5i} = $

32) $\dfrac{-6 - i}{-1 + 6i} = $

33) $\dfrac{-9 - 3i}{-3 + 3i} = $

34) $\dfrac{4i + 1}{-1 + 3i} = $

✍️ *Evaluate each function.*

35) $f(x) = x - 2$, find $f(1)$

36) $g(x) = 2x + 3$, find $g(2)$

37) $h(x) = x + 8$, find $h(5)$

38) $h(n) = n^2 + 4$, find $h(-4)$

39) $h(n) = n^2 - 10$, find $h(5)$

40) $h(n) = -2n^2 - 6n$, find $h(2)$

✍️ *Perform the indicated operation.*

41) $g(a) = -3a - 3$

$\quad f(a) = a^2 + 5$

$\quad$ Find $(g - f)(a)$

42) $g(t) = 2t + 5$

$\quad f(t) = -t^2 + 5$

$\quad$ Find $(g + f)(t)$

✍️ *Perform the indicated operation.*

43) $g(x) = -x - 2$

$\quad f(x) = 2x + 1$

$\quad$ Find $(g.f)(2)$

44) $f(x) = 3x$

$\quad h(x) = -2x + 5$

$\quad$ Find $(f.h)(-1)$

✍️ *Using $f(x) = 5x + 4$ and $g(x) = x - 3$, find:*

45) $g\big(f(-3)\big) =$

46) $g\big(f(4)\big) =$

47) $f\big(g(6)\big) =$

48) $f\big(f(8)\big) =$

✍️ *Find the exact value of each trigonometric function. Some may be undefined.*

49) $\sec \pi =$

50) $\tan -\dfrac{3\pi}{2} =$

51) $\cos \dfrac{11\pi}{6} =$

52) $\cot \dfrac{5\pi}{3} =$

53) $\sec -\dfrac{3\pi}{4} =$

54) $\sec \dfrac{\pi}{3} =$

✍️ *Convert each degree measure into radians and each radian measure into degrees.*

55) $420° =$ ____

56) $300° =$ ____

57) $-60° =$ ___

58) $-\dfrac{16\pi}{3} =$

59) $-\dfrac{3\pi}{5} =$

60) $\dfrac{11\pi}{6} =$

✍️ *Use the given point on the terminal side of angle θ to find the value of the trigonometric function indicated.*

61) $\sin\theta,\ (-6, 4)$

62) $\cos\theta,\ (2, -2)$

63) $\cot\theta,\ (-7, \sqrt{15})$

64) $\cos\theta,\ (-5, -12)$

65) $\sin\theta,\ (-\sqrt{7}, 3)$

66) $\tan\theta,\ (-11, -2)$

Answers

1) $x = 0, y = -3$
2) $x = -2, y = -4$
3) $x = 4, y = -2$
4) $x = 5, y = -7$
5) $(x - 4)(x - 1)$
6) $(x + 4)(x + 2)$
7) $(x - 3)(x + 4)$
8) $(x - 5)(x - 2)$
9) $(x + 2)(x - 6)$
10) $(2x + 1)(x - 2)$
11) $x < -5 \, or \, x > 1$
12) $x \leq -1 \, or \, x \geq 3$
13) $-1 < x < 1$
14) $x \leq -1 \, or \, x \geq \frac{2}{17}$
15) $-\frac{11}{2} < x < \frac{1}{2}$
16) $x < -\frac{3}{2} \, or \, x > \frac{2}{3}$
17) $6 + 7i$
18) $-2 + 12i$
19) $-2 + 12i$
20) $-7 + 2i$
21) $-2 - 6i$
22) $-16 + 8i$
23) $-7 - 6i$
24) $-8i$
25) $6 - 42i$
26) $-\frac{27}{113} - \frac{47}{113}i$
27) $-\frac{59}{53} + \frac{32}{53}i$
28) $\frac{3}{29} + \frac{22}{29}i$
29) $-i$
30) $-\frac{1}{9}i$
31) $\frac{-8}{5}i$
32) i
33) $1 + 2i$
34) $\frac{11}{10} - \frac{7}{10}i$

35) -1
36) 7
37) 13
38) 20
39) 15
40) -20
41) $-a^2 - 3a - 8$
42) $-t^2 + 2t + 10$
43) -20
44) -21
45) -14
46) 21
47) 19
48) 224
49) -1
50) Undefined
51) $\frac{\sqrt{3}}{2}$
52) $-\frac{\sqrt{3}}{3}$
53) $-\sqrt{2}$
54) 2
55) $\frac{7\pi}{3}$
56) $\frac{5\pi}{3}$
57) $-\frac{\pi}{3}$
58) $-960°$
59) $-108°$
60) $330°$
61) $\frac{2\sqrt{13}}{13}$
62) $\sqrt{2}$
63) $-\frac{7\sqrt{15}}{15}$
64) $-\frac{5}{13}$
65) $\frac{3}{4}$
66) $\frac{2}{11}$

Time to Test

Time to refine your skill with a practice examination

Take a REAL ALEKS Mathematics test to simulate the test day experience. After you've finished, score your test using the answers and explanations section.

Before You Start

- You'll need a pencil and scratch papers to take the test.

- For these practice tests, don't time yourself. Spend time as much as you need.

- After you've finished the test, review the answer key to see where you went wrong.

Good Luck!

ALEKS Mathematics
Practice Test 1

2019 - 2020

Total number of questions: 30

Total time: No time limit

Calculators are permitted for ALEKS Math Test.

(On a real ALEKS test, there is an onscreen calculator to use.)

1) How many tiles of $8 \ cm^2$ is needed to cover a floor of dimension $6 \ cm$ by $24 \ cm$?

2) What is the area of a square whose diagonal is $8 \ cm$?

3) What is the value of x in the following figure?

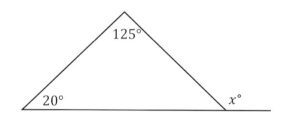

4) What is the value of y in the following system of equation?
$$3x - 4y = -20$$
$$-x + 2y = 10$$

5) How long does a 420–miles trip take moving at 50 miles per hour (mph)?

6) When 40% of 60 is added to 12% of 600, the resulting number is:

7) What is the solution of the following inequality?
$$|x - 10| \leq 3$$

8) In the following figure, ABCD is a rectangle, and E and F are points on AD and DC, respectively. The area of ΔBED is 16, and the area of ΔBDF is 18. What is the perimeter of the rectangle?

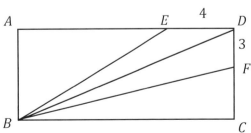

9) If a tree casts a 24–foot shadow at the same time that a 3 feet yardstick casts a 2–foot shadow, what is the height of the tree?

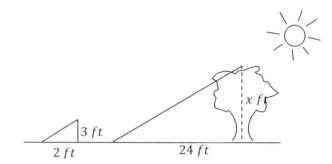

10) A ladder leans against a wall forming a $60°$ angle between the ground and the ladder. If the bottom of the ladder is 30 feet away from the wall, how long is the ladder?

11) Simplify.

$$2x^2 + 3y^5 - x^2 + 2z^3 - 2y^2 + 2x^3 - 2y^5 + 5z^3$$

12) In five successive hours, a car traveled $40\ km, 45\ km, 50\ km, 35\ km$ and $55\ km$. In the next five hours, it traveled with an average speed of $50\ km\ per\ hour$. Find the total distance the car traveled in 10 hours.

13) In the following figure, ABCD is a rectangle. If $a = \sqrt{3}$, and $b = 2a$, find the area of the shaded region. (the shaded region is a trapezoid)

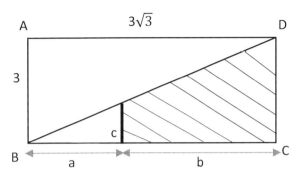

14) 6 liters of water are poured into an aquarium that's $15cm$ long, $5cm$ wide, and $90cm$ high. How many centimeters will the water level in the aquarium rise due to this added water? ($1\ liter\ of\ water = 1,000\ cm^3$)

15) If a box contains red and blue balls in ratio of $2:3$, how many red balls are there if 90 blue balls are in the box?

16) A chemical solution contains 4% alcohol. If there is 24 ml of alcohol, what is the volume of the solution?

17) If $\frac{3x}{16} = \frac{x-1}{4}$, $x =$

18) Simplify $(-5 + 9i)(3 + 5i)$.

19) If θ is an acute angle and $sin\ \theta = \frac{4}{5}$ then $cos\ \theta =$

20) If 60% of x equal to 30% of 20, then what is the value of $(x + 5)^2$?

21) A boat sails 40 miles south and then 30 miles east. How far is the boat from its start point?

22) What is the value of x in the following equation? $log_4(x + 2) - log_4(x - 2) = 1$

23) A number is chosen at random from 1 to 25. Find the probability of not selecting a composite number.

24) Find AC in the following triangle. Round answers to the nearest tenth.

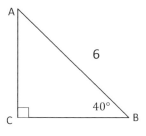

25) If $y = 4ab + 3b^3$, what is y when $a = 2$ and $b = 3$?

26) If $f(x) = 5 + x$ and $g(x) = -x^2 - 1 - 2x$, then find $(g - f)(x)$.

27) If cotangent of an angel β is 1, then the tangent of angle β is …

28) When point A $(10, 3)$ is reflected over the y −axis to get the point B, what are the coordinates of point B?

29) What is the average of circumference of figure A and area of figure B? ($\pi = 3$)

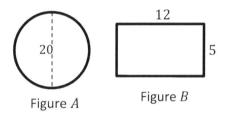

Figure A Figure B

30) If $f(x) = 2x^3 + 5x^2 + 2x$ and $g(x) = -2$, what is the value of $f(g(x))$?

This is the end of Practice Test 1.

ALEKS Mathematics Practice Test 2

2019 - 2020

Total number of questions: 30

Total time: No time limit

Calculators are permitted for ALEKS Math Test.

(On a real ALEKS test, there is an onscreen calculator to use.)

1) If $f(x) = 3x - 1$ and $g(x) = x^2 - x$, then find $(\frac{f}{g})(x)$.

2) A bank is offering 3.5% simple interest on a savings account. If you deposit $12,000, how much interest will you earn in two years?

3) If the ratio of home fans to visiting fans in a crowd is $3 : 2$ and all 25,000 seats in a stadium are filled, how many visiting fans are in attendance?

4) If the interior angles of a quadrilateral are in the ratio $1 : 2 : 3 : 4$, what is the measure of the largest angle?

5) If the area of a circle is 64 square meters, what is its diameter?

6) The length of a rectangle is $\frac{5}{4}$ times its width. If the width is 16, what is the perimeter of this rectangle?

7) In the figure below, line A is parallel to line B. What is the value of angle x?

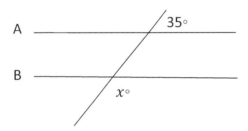

8) An angle is equal to one fifth of its supplement. What is the measure of that angle?

9) What is the value of x in the following system of equations?
$$2x + 5y = 11$$
$$4x - 2y = -14$$

10) Last week 24,000 fans attended a football match. This week three times as many bought tickets, but one sixth of them cancelled their tickets. How many are attending this week?

11) If $sin\ A = \frac{1}{4}$ in a right triangle and the angle A is an acute angle, then what is $cos\ A$?

12) In the standard (x, y) coordinate system plane, what is the area of the circle with the following equation?
$$(x + 2)^2 + (y - 4)^2 = 16$$

13) Convert 670,000 to scientific notation.

14) The ratio of boys to girls in a school is 2: 3. If there are 600 students in a school, how many boys are in the school.

15) If 150% of a number is 75, then what is 90% of that number?

16) If $A = \begin{bmatrix} -1 & 2 \\ 1 & -2 \end{bmatrix}$ and $B = \begin{bmatrix} 4 & 1 \\ -2 & 3 \end{bmatrix}$, then $2A - B =$

17) What is the solution of the following inequality?
$$|x - 2| \geq 3$$

18) If $\tan x = \dfrac{8}{15}$, then $\sin x =$

19) $\left(x^6\right)^{\frac{5}{8}}$ equal to?

20) What are the zeroes of the function $f(x) = x^3 + 6x^2 + 8x$?

21) If $x + sin^2 a + cos^2 a = 3$, then x = ?

22) If $\sqrt{6x} = \sqrt{y}$, then $x =$

23) The average weight of 18 girls in a class is $60 \ kg$ and the average weight of 32 boys in the same class is $62 \ kg$. What is the average weight of all the 50 students in that class?

24) What is the value of the expression $5(x - 2y) + (2 - x)^2$ when $x = 3$ and $y = -2$?

25) Sophia purchased a sofa for $530.40. The sofa is regularly priced at $624. What was the percent discount Sophia received on the sofa?

26) If one angle of a right triangle measures $60°$, what is the sine of the other acute angle?

27) Simplify $\dfrac{5-3i}{-5i}$?

28) The average of five consecutive numbers is 38. What is the smallest number?

29) What is the slope of a line that is perpendicular to the line
$$4x - 2y = 12?$$

30) If $f(x) = 2x^4 + 2$ and $(x) = \frac{1}{x}$, what is the value of $f(g(x))$?

This is the end of Practice Test 2.

ALEKS Mathematics Practice Tests
Answers and Explanations

Now, it's time to review your results to see where you went wrong and what areas you need to improve!

ALEKS Mathematics Practice Test 1

1) The answer is 18

The area of the floor is: $6\ cm \times 24\ cm = 144\ cm^2$. The number is tiles needed $= 144 \div 8 = 18$

2) The answer is 32

The diagonal of the square is 8. Let x be the side.

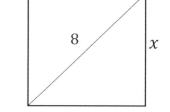

Use Pythagorean Theorem: $a^2 + b^2 = c^2$

$x^2 + x^2 = 8^2 \Rightarrow 2x^2 = 8^2 \Rightarrow 2x^2 = 64 \Rightarrow x^2 = 32 \Rightarrow x = \sqrt{32}$

The area of the square is: $\sqrt{32} \times \sqrt{32} = 32$

3) The answer is 145

$x = 20 + 125 = 145$

4) The answer is 5

Solve the system of equations by elimination method.

$3x - 4y = -20$
$\underline{-x + 2y = 10}$ Multiply the second equation by 3, then add it to the first equation.

$\begin{array}{l} 3x - 4y = -20 \\ \underline{3(-x + 2y = 10)} \end{array} \Rightarrow \begin{array}{l} 3x - 4y = -20 \\ -3x + 6y = 30) \end{array} \Rightarrow$ add the equations $2y = 10 \Rightarrow y = 5$

5) The answer is 8.4 hours

Use distance formula: $Distance = Rate \times time \Rightarrow 420 = 50 \times T$, divide both sides by

50. $420 \div 50 = T \Rightarrow T = 8.4\ hours$. Change hours to minutes for the decimal part. $0.4\ hours = 0.4 \times 60 = 24\ minutes$.

6) The answer is 96

40% of 60 equals to: $0.40 \times 60 = 24$, 12% of 600 equals to: $0.12 \times 600 = 72$

40% of 60 is added to 12% of 600: $24 + 72 = 96$

7) **The answer is** $7 \leq x \leq 13$

$|x - 10| \leq 3 \rightarrow -3 \leq x - 10 \leq 3 \rightarrow -3 + 10 \leq x - 10 + 10 \leq 3 + 10 \rightarrow 7 \leq x \leq 13$

8) **The answer is 40**

The area of ΔBED is 16, then: $\frac{4 \times AB}{2} = 16 \rightarrow 4 \times AB = 32 \rightarrow AB = 8$

The area of ΔBDF is 18, then: $\frac{3 \times BC}{2} = 18 \rightarrow 3 \times BC = 36 \rightarrow BC = 12$

The perimeter of the rectangle is $= 2 \times (8 + 12) = 40$

9) **The answer is** $36\,ft$

Write a proportion and solve for x. $\frac{3}{2} = \frac{x}{24} \Rightarrow 2x = 3 \times 24 \Rightarrow x = 36\,ft$

10) **The answer is** $60\,ft$

The relationship among all sides of special right triangle

$30° - 60° - 90°$ is provided in this triangle:

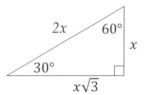

In this triangle, the opposite side of 30° angle is half of the hypotenuse.

Draw the shape of this question:

The latter is the hypotenuse. Therefore, the latter is $60\,ft$.

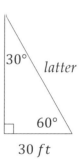

11) **The answer is** $y^5 + 2x^3 + 7z^3 + x^2 - 2y^2$

$2x^2 + 3y^5 - x^2 + 2z^3 - 2y^2 + 2x^3 - 2y^5 + 5z^3$
$= 2x^2 - x^2 + 2x^3 - 2y^2 + 3y^5 - 2y^5 + 2z^3 + 5z^3$
$= x^2 + 2x^3 - 2y^2 + y^5 + 7z^3$

Write the expression in standard form:

$x^2 + 2x^3 - 2y^2 + y^5 + 7z^3 = y^5 + 2x^3 + 7z^3 + x^2 - 2y^2$

12) **The answer is** 475

Add the first 5 numbers. $40 + 45 + 50 + 35 + 55 = 225$

To find the distance traveled in the next 5 hours, multiply the average by number of hours.

$Distance = Average \times Rate = 50 \times 5 = 250$. Add both numbers. $250 + 225 = 475$

13) **The answer is** $4\sqrt{3}$

Based on triangle similarity theorem: $\frac{a}{a+b} = \frac{c}{3} \to c = \frac{3a}{a+b} = \frac{3\sqrt{3}}{3\sqrt{3}} = 1 \to$ area of shaded region is:

$\left(\frac{c+3}{2}\right)(b) = \frac{4}{2} \times 2\sqrt{3} = 4\sqrt{3}$

14) The answer is $80cm$

One liter $= 1,000 \ cm^3 \to$ *6 liters* $= 6,000 \ cm^3$ $6,000 = 15 \times 5 \times h \to h = \frac{6,000}{75} = 80cm$

15) The answer is 60

$\frac{2}{3} \times 90 = 60$

16) The answer is $600 \ ml$

4% of the volume of the solution is alcohol. Let x be the volume of the solution.

Then: $4\% \ of \ x = 24 \ ml \ \Rightarrow \ 0.04 \ x = 24 \ \Rightarrow \ x = 24 \div 0.04 = 600$

17) The answer is 4

Solve for x. $\frac{3x}{16} = \frac{x-1}{4}$. Multiply the second fraction by 4. $\frac{3x}{16} = \frac{4(x-1)}{4\times 4}$. Tow denominators are equal. Therefore, the numerators must be equal. $3x = 4x - 4, \quad 0 = x - 4, 4 = x$

18) The answer is $-60 + 2i$

We know that: $i = \sqrt{-1} \Rightarrow i^2 = -1$

$(-5 + 9i)(3 + 5i) = -15 - 25i + 27i + 45i^2 = -15 + 2i - 45 = -60 + 2i$

19) The answer is $\frac{3}{5}$

$sin\theta = \frac{4}{5} \Rightarrow$ we have following triangle, then

$c = \sqrt{5^2 - 4^2} = \sqrt{25 - 16} = \sqrt{9} = 3, cos\theta = \frac{3}{5}$

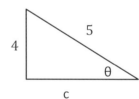

20) The answer is 225

$0.6x = (0.3) \times 20 \to x = 10 \to (x + 5)^2 = (15)^2 = 225$

21) The answer is $50 \ miles$

Use the information provided in the question to draw the shape.

Use Pythagorean Theorem: $a^2 + b^2 = c^2$

$40^2 + 30^2 = c^2 \ \Rightarrow \ 1,600 + 900 = c^2 \ \Rightarrow \ 2,500 = c^2 \ \Rightarrow \ c = 50$

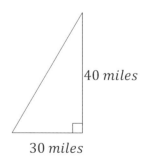

22) The answer is $\frac{10}{3}$

METHOD ONE

$log_4(x + 2) - log_4(x - 2) = 1$, Add $log_4(x - 2)$ to both sides

$log_4(x + 2) - log_4(x - 2) + log_4(x - 2) = 1 + log_4(x - 2)$

$log_4(x + 2) = 1 + log_4(x - 2)$

Apply logarithm rule: $a = log_b(b^a) \Rightarrow 1 = log_4(4^1) = log_4(4)$

then: $log_4(x + 2) = log_4(4) + log_4(x - 2)$

Logarithm rule: $log_c(a) + log_c(b) = log_c(ab)$

then: $log_4(4) + log_4(x - 2) = log_4(4(x - 2))$

$log_4(x + 2) = log_4(4(x - 2))$

When the logs have the same base: $log_b(f(x)) = log_b(g(x)) = f(x) = g(x)$

$(x + 2) = 4(x - 2), x = \dfrac{10}{3}$

METHOD TWO

We know that: $log_a b - log_a c = log_a \dfrac{b}{c}$ and $log_a b = c \Rightarrow b = a^c$

Then: $log_4(x + 2) - log_4(x - 2) = log_4 \dfrac{x+2}{x-2} = 1 \Rightarrow \dfrac{x+2}{x-2} = 4^1 = 4 \Rightarrow x + 2 = 4(x - 2)$

$\Rightarrow x + 2 = 4x - 8 \Rightarrow 4x - x = 8 + 2 \rightarrow 3x = 10 \Rightarrow x = \dfrac{10}{3}$

23) The answer is $\dfrac{2}{5}$

Set of number that are not composite between 1 and 25: $A = \{1, 2, 3, 5, 7, 11, 13, 17, 19, 23\}$

$Probability = \dfrac{number\ of\ desired\ outcomes}{number\ of\ total\ outcomes} = \dfrac{10}{25} = \dfrac{2}{5}$

24) The answer is 3.9

$sine\ \theta = \dfrac{opposite}{hypotenuse}$. $sine\ 40° = \dfrac{AC}{6} \rightarrow 6 \times sine\ 40° = AC$,

now use a calculator to find $sine\ 40°$. $sine\ 40° \cong 0.642 \rightarrow AC \cong 3.9$

25) The answer is 105

$y = 4ab + 3b^3$. Plug in the values of a and b in the equation: $a = 2$ and $b = 3$

$y = 4(2)(3) + 3(3)^3 = 24 + 3(27) = 24 + 81 = 105$

26) The answer is $-x^2 - 3x - 6$

$(g - f)(x) = g(x) - f(x) = (-x^2 - 1 - 2x) - (5 + x)$

$-x^2 - 1 - 2x - 5 - x = -x^2 - 3x - 6$

27) The answer is 1

$$tangent\ \beta = \frac{1}{cotangent\ \beta} = \frac{1}{1} = 1$$

28) The answer is $(-10, 3)$

When points are reflected over y-axis, the value of y in the coordinates doesn't change and the sign of x changes. Therefore, the coordinates of point B is $(-10, 3)$.

29) The answer is 60

Perimeter of figure A is: $2\pi r = 2\pi \frac{20}{2} = 20\pi = 20 \times 3 = 60$

Area of figure B is: $5 \times 12 = 60$, $Average = \frac{60+60}{2} = \frac{120}{2} = 60$

30) The answer is 0

$g(x) = -2,$ **then** $f\big(g(x)\big) = f(-2) = 2\,(-2)^3 + 5(-2)^2 + 2(-2) = -16 + 20 - 4 = 0$

ALEKS Mathematics Practice Test 2

1) The answer is $\frac{3x-1}{x^2-x}$

$$\left(\frac{f}{g}\right)(x) = \frac{f(x)}{g(x)} = \frac{3x-1}{x^2-x}$$

2) The answer is 840

Use simple interest formula: $I = prt$ ($I = $ interest, $p = $ principal, $r = $ rate, $t = $ time)

$$I = (12{,}000)(0.035)(2) = 840$$

3) The answer is $10{,}000$

Number of visiting fans: $\quad \frac{2 \times 25{,}000}{5} = 10{,}000$

4) The answer is $144°$

The sum of all angles in a quadrilateral is 360 degrees. Let x be the smallest angle in the quadrilateral. Then the angles are: $x, 2x, 3x, 4x, x + 2x + 3x + 4x = 360 \to 10x = 360 \to x = 36$, The angles in the quadrilateral are: $36°, 72°, 108°,$ and $144°$

5) The answer is $\frac{8\sqrt{\pi}}{\pi}$

Formula for the area of a circle is: $A = \pi r^2$, Using 64 for the area of the circle we have: $64 = \pi r^2$. Let's solve for the radius (r). $\frac{64}{\pi} = r^2 \to r = \sqrt{\frac{64}{\pi}} = \frac{8}{\sqrt{\pi}} = \frac{8}{\sqrt{\pi}} \times \frac{\sqrt{\pi}}{\sqrt{\pi}} = \frac{8\sqrt{\pi}}{\pi}$

6) The answer is 72

Length of the rectangle is: $\frac{5}{4} \times 16 = 20$, perimeter of rectangle is: $2 \times (20 + 16) = 72$

7) The answer is $145°$

The angle x and 35 are complementary angles. Therefore: $x + 35 = 180 \to$

$$x = 180° - 35° = 145°$$

8) The answer is 30

The sum of supplement angles is 180. Let x be that angle. Therefore, $x + 5x = 180$
$6x = 180$, divide both sides by 6: $x = 30$

9) The answer is -2

Solving Systems of Equations by Elimination: Multiply the first equation by (-2), then add it to the second equation.

$$\begin{array}{l} -2(2x + 5y = 11) \\ \underline{4x - 2y = -14} \end{array} \Rightarrow \begin{array}{l} -4x - 10y = -22 \\ 4x - 2y = -14 \end{array} \Rightarrow -12y = -36 \Rightarrow y = 3$$

Plug in the value of y into one of the equations and solve for x.

$$2x + 5(3) = 11 \Rightarrow 2x + 15 = 11 \Rightarrow 2x = -4 \Rightarrow x = -2$$

10) The answer is $60,000$

Three times of 24,000 is 72,000. One sixth of them cancelled their tickets. One sixth of 72,000 equals 12,000 ($\frac{1}{6} \times 72,000 = 12,000$). 60,000 (72,000 $-$ 12,000 $=$ 60,000) fans are attending this week.

11) The answer is $\frac{\sqrt{15}}{4}$

$sinA = \frac{1}{4} \Rightarrow$ Since $sin\theta = \frac{opposite}{hypotenuse}$, we have the following right triangle. Then:

$c = \sqrt{4^2 - 1^2} = \sqrt{16 - 1} = \sqrt{15}, cosA = \frac{\sqrt{15}}{4}$

12) The answer is 16π

The equation of a circle in standard form is: $(x - h)^2 + (y - k)^2 = r^2$, where r is the radius of the circle. In this circle the radius is 4. $r^2 = 16 \rightarrow r = 4$, $(x + 2)^2 + (y - 4)^2 = 16$, Area of a circle: $A = \pi r^2 = \pi(4)^2 = 16\pi$

13) The answer is 6.7×10^5

$670,000 = 6.7 \times 10^5$

14) The answer is 240

The ratio of boy to girls is $2:3$. Therefore, there are 2 boys out of 5 students. To find the answer, first divide the total number of students by 5, then multiply the result by 2.

$$600 \div 5 = 120 \Rightarrow 120 \times 2 = 240$$

15) The answer is 45

First, find the number. Let x be the number. Write the equation and solve for x. 150% of a number is 75, then: $1.5 \times x = 75 \Rightarrow x = 75 \div 1.5 = 50$, 90% of 50 is: $0.9 \times 50 = 45$

16) The answer is $\begin{bmatrix} -6 & 3 \\ 4 & -7 \end{bmatrix}$

First, find $2A$. $A = \begin{bmatrix} -1 & 2 \\ 1 & -2 \end{bmatrix}$ $\qquad 2A = 2 \times \begin{bmatrix} -1 & 2 \\ 1 & -2 \end{bmatrix} = \begin{bmatrix} -2 & 4 \\ 2 & -4 \end{bmatrix}$

Now, solve for $2A - B$.

$$2A - B = \begin{bmatrix} -2 & 4 \\ 2 & -4 \end{bmatrix} - \begin{bmatrix} 4 & 1 \\ -2 & 3 \end{bmatrix} = \begin{bmatrix} -2-4 & 4-1 \\ 2-(-2) & -4-3 \end{bmatrix} = \begin{bmatrix} -6 & 3 \\ 4 & -7 \end{bmatrix}$$

17) The answer is $x \geq 5 \cup x \leq -1$

$x - 2 \geq 3 \rightarrow x \geq 3 + 2 \rightarrow x \geq 5$, Or $x - 2 \leq -3 \rightarrow x \leq -3 + 2 \rightarrow x \leq -1$

Then, solution is: $\quad x \geq 5 \cup x \leq -1$

18) The answer is $\frac{8}{17}$

$\tan = \frac{opposite}{adjacent}$, and $\tan x = \frac{8}{15}$, therefore, the opposite side of the angle x is 8 and the adjacent side is 15. Let's draw the triangle.

Using Pythagorean theorem, we have: $a^2 + b^2 = c^2 \rightarrow 8^2 + 15^2 = c^2 \rightarrow 64 + 225 = c^2 \rightarrow$
$c = 17$, $\sin x = \frac{opposite}{hypotenuse} = \frac{8}{17}$

19) The answer is $x^{\frac{15}{4}}$

$(x^6)^{\frac{5}{8}} = x^{6 \times \frac{5}{8}} = x^{\frac{30}{8}} = x^{\frac{15}{4}}$

20) The answer are $0, -2, -3$

Frist factor the function: $f(x) = x^3 + 6x^2 + 8x = x(x+4)(x+2)$, **To find the zeros,** $f(x)$ **should be zero.** $f(x) = x(x+4)(x+2) = 0$, **Therefore, the zeros are:** $x = 0$, $\quad (x+4) = 0 \Rightarrow \quad x = -4$, $(x+2) = 0 \Rightarrow x = -2$

21) The answer is 2

$\sin^2 a + \cos^2 a = 1$, then: $x + 1 = 3$, $\qquad x = 2$

22) The answer is $\frac{y}{6}$

Solve for x. $\sqrt{6x} = \sqrt{y}$. $\qquad$ Square both sides of the equation:

$(\sqrt{6x})^2 = (\sqrt{y})^2 \qquad 6x = y \qquad x = \frac{y}{6}$

23) The answer is 61.28

$average = \frac{sum\ of\ terms}{number\ of\ terms}$, The sum of the weight of all girls is: $18 \times 60 = 1,080\ kg$

The sum of the weight of all boys is: $32 \times 62 = 1,984\ kg$, The sum of the weight of all students is: $1,080 + 1,984 = 3,064\ kg$. $average = \frac{3,064}{50} = 61.28$

24) The answer is 36

Plug in the value of x and y. $x = 3$ and $y = -2$

$5(x - 2y) + (2 - x)^2 = 5(3 - 2(-2)) + (2 - 3)^2 = 5(3 + 4) + (-1)^2 = 35 + 1 = 36$

25) The answer is 15%

The question is this: 530.40 is what percent of 624?

Use percent formula: $part = \frac{percent}{100} \times whole$

$530.40 = \frac{percent}{100} \times 624 \Rightarrow 530.40 = \frac{percent \times 624}{100} \Rightarrow 53,040 = percent \times 624 \Rightarrow$

$percent = \frac{53,040}{624} = 85$. 530.40 is 85% of 624. Therefore, the discount is: $100\% - 85\% = 15\%$

26) The answer is $\frac{1}{2}$

The relationship among all sides of right triangle $30° - 60° - 90°$ is provided in the following triangle:

Sine of $30°$ equals to: $\frac{opposite}{hypotenuse} = \frac{x}{2x} = \frac{1}{2}$

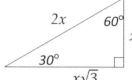

27) The answer is $\frac{3}{5} + i$

To simplify the fraction, multiply both numerator and denominator by i.

$\frac{5-3i}{-5i} \times \frac{i}{i} = \frac{5i-3i^2}{-5i^2}$, $i^2 - 1$, Then: $\frac{5i-3i^2}{-5i^2} = \frac{5i-3(-1)}{-5(-1)} = \frac{5i+3}{5} = \frac{5i}{5} + \frac{3}{5} = \frac{3}{5} + i$

28) The answer is 36

Let x be the smallest number. Then, these are the numbers: $x, x + 1, x + 2, x + 3, x + 4$

$average = \frac{sum\ of\ terms}{number\ of\ terms} \Rightarrow 38 = \frac{x+(x+1)+(x+2)+(x+3)+(x+4)}{5} \Rightarrow 38 = \frac{5x+10}{5} \Rightarrow$

$190 = 5x + 10 \Rightarrow 180 = 5x \Rightarrow x = 36$

29) The answer is $-\frac{1}{2}$

The equation of a line in slope intercept form is: $y = mx + b$. Solve for y. $4x - 2y = 12 \Rightarrow$
$-2y = 12 - 4x \Rightarrow y = (12 - 4x) \div (-2) \Rightarrow y = 2x - 6$

The slope is 2. The slope of the line perpendicular to this line is:

$m_1 \times m_2 = -1 \Rightarrow 2 \times m_2 = -1 \Rightarrow m_2 = -\frac{1}{2}$

30) The answer is $\frac{2}{x^4} + 2$

$f(g(x)) = 2 \times (\frac{1}{x})^4 + 2 = \frac{2}{x^4} + 2$

"Effortless Math" Publications

Effortless Math authors' team strives to prepare and publish the best quality Mathematics learning resources to make learning Math easier for all. We hope that our publications help you or your student Math in an effective way.

We all in Effortless Math wish you good luck and successful studies!

Effortless Math Authors

www.EffortlessMath.com

… So Much More Online!

✓ FREE Math lessons

✓ More Math learning books!

✓ Mathematics Worksheets

✓ Online Math Tutors

Need a PDF version of this book?

Visit www.EffortlessMath.com

Made in the USA
Columbia, SC
02 July 2021